LEARN MATH FAST
VOLUME II
THIRD EDITION

By J.K. Mergens

Learn Math Fast System Vol. II Third Edition
Copyright © 2011 Registration Number TX 7-316-060
ISBN: 978-0-9843814-4-9
www.LearnMathFastBooks.com

TABLE OF CONTENTS

Welcome to Volume II of the *Learn Math Fast System*. This system works best if you start with Volume I, but if you already know how to add, subtract, multiply, and divide, with decimal points, then you can start with Volume II. Read each lesson and then complete the worksheet at the end of each lesson. Be sure to compare your answers to the ones in the back of the book. If you get 2 or more problems incorrect, read the lesson one more time and try again.

If you ever have any questions or comments, please contact us at our website www.LearnMathFastBooks.com.

CHAPTER 1

FRACTIONS

Fractions are a stumbling block for a lot of math students. Everyone gets confused when it comes to learning fractions. I will teach you how to write, understand, add, subtract, multiply, and divide fractions; in a *fraction* of the time you might expect.

Can you solve these problems?

9/16 - 2/8 =
4/10 + 1/5 =
3/9 x 2/5 =

Read this chapter and in about an hour not only will these problems be easy for you, but you'll be able to solve them in your head.

LESSON 1: BEGINNING FRACTIONS

First of all, what is a fraction? A fraction is a piece of something. If I broke a vase into 100 pieces and then picked up 1 of the pieces, I would be holding a *fraction* of the vase.

You can also look at a fraction as a number between zero and one. A fraction is a piece of 1 whole something. Here are a few more fractions you will recognize:

- A penny is a *fraction* of one dollar.
- A second is a *fraction* of one minute.
- A slice of pizza is a *fraction* of the whole pizza.
- An inch is a *fraction* of one foot.
- Your leg is a *fraction* of you!

Let's start with a dollar bill because it has a "1" written right on it, so it will represent ONE.

Now let's divide that dollar into ten pieces. We all know what that would be; DIMES!

If we broke up one dollar into dimes, we would have ten dimes. Ten dimes equal one dollar.

Each dime is $\frac{1}{10}$ (one tenth) of the dollar. Look at that fraction.

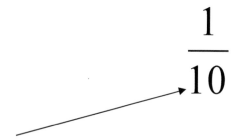

$$\frac{1}{10}$$

The "10" on the bottom is how many dimes it takes to make 1 dollar. The "1" on top represents 1 dime.

One dime is one tenth $\left(\frac{1}{10}\right)$ of the dollar. It is a fraction of the dollar.
Think of the fraction $\frac{1}{10}$ as *one of the ten pieces*.

Two dimes would be written like this...

$$\frac{2}{10}$$

because we have two of the ten pieces.

Let's try another fraction. This time instead of breaking up the dollar into dimes, we will break it up into quarters. How many quarters are in a dollar? That's right, four.

Each quarter is one of the four pieces that you need to make one dollar, so each one is written as $\frac{1}{4}$. You can say "one fourth" or "one quarter," either one is correct. Now you know why twenty five cents is called a quarter; because it's a quarter of a dollar.

Sometimes fractions are written with a slanted line like $\frac{1}{4}$. Other times they are written with one number on top, one number on bottom, and a straight line in between them; like the one below.

$$\frac{1}{4}$$

Either way it means the same thing, one of four the pieces.

How would you write *one penny* as a fraction?

Think about how many pennies are in a dollar. There are one hundred, so that is the number on the bottom of the fraction. We are talking about only one penny, so that is the number on the top of the fraction.

$$\frac{1}{100}$$

To read this fraction, say *one-one hundredth*. A penny is one-one hundredth of a dollar.

How would you write 2 pennies as a fraction? There are 100 pennies in 1 dollar, so that is the number on the bottom. The 2 goes on top.

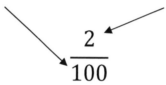

$$\frac{2}{100}$$

Here's a tricky question. How many dollars would you have, if you had 100/100? Well, let's think about that. If you had 100 of the 100 pennies, that would be 1 whole dollar.

$$\frac{100}{100} = 1$$

Now let's say you had 4/4 of a dollar. How many dollars would you have?

$$\frac{4}{4} = 1$$

Well, if the bottom number is 4, and the top number is 4, then we have all 4 pieces to make 1 dollar. Any time the number on top is the same as the number on bottom, it equals 1.

Let's say I sliced a candy bar into 4 equal pieces. I want to write a fraction to show how much of the candy bar I have eaten.

The number on the bottom of the fraction will show how many pieces there are in one candy bar.

$$\frac{\quad}{4}$$

The number on top will be how many of the 4 pieces I ate. I ate all 4 pieces, so put that number on top.

$$\frac{4}{4}$$

How many candy bars did I eat? You could say I ate four-fourths of the candy bar, but that sounds a little goofy. Let's just say I ate one candy bar.

$$\frac{4}{4} = 1$$

Answer the questions on the next worksheet, to make sure you understand what a fraction means.

Name: _____   Date: _____

WORKSHEET 2-1

1. Which of the following are fractions?

$$36 \qquad 42.9 \qquad \frac{2}{5} \qquad 0 \qquad \frac{1}{100}$$

2. A dime is $\frac{1}{10}$ of a dollar and a quarter is $\frac{1}{4}$ of a dollar. Can you write a fraction for one penny?

3. What does the number on the bottom of a fraction mean?

4. Give a number that is equal to $\frac{25}{25}$.

5. Write a fraction of a dollar that equals 2 dimes.

6. Write the fraction that represents the picture below.

7. Write a fraction that equals 1.

8. I bought a pack of gum. There were 10 pieces in the pack. I gave my sister 3 of the pieces. Write a fraction that shows how much gum I have left in the pack.

9. Which fraction is bigger? Use a $<$ or $>$ sign.
$$\frac{1}{4} \underline{\qquad} \frac{1}{100}$$

10. Write a fraction that stands for 3 cents.

So now that you know what fractions are, let's have some fun with them. I have 5 pennies and you have 2 pennies. To add them together, use fractions like this:

$$\frac{5}{100} + \frac{2}{100} =$$

Now we don't want to add the 100's together because the amount of pennies in a dollar can't change. Just add up the top numbers, 5 + 2 = 7 and the answer is...

$$\frac{7}{100}$$

You just added fractions! Remember, the number on top is how many pennies and the number on bottom is how many pennies it takes to make one.

Next, we will add 1 quarter (think money) and 2 quarters. Look at the math and the pictures below.

$$\frac{1}{4} \quad + \quad \frac{2}{4}$$

To add fractions, just add the numbers on top. You can't change the number of quarters in one dollar, so the only math to solve is 1 + 2.

$$\frac{1}{4} + \frac{2}{4} = \frac{3}{4}$$

Try adding fractions on your own. Complete the next worksheet. If you don't get 100% correct, read this lesson again.

Name: _____   Date: _____

WORKSHEET 2-2

Add the following fractions.

1. $\frac{3}{8} + \frac{3}{8} =$ 2. $\frac{5}{21} + \frac{9}{21} =$

3. $\frac{1}{4} + \frac{2}{4} =$ 4. $\frac{3}{10} + \frac{4}{10} =$

5. $\frac{5}{12} + \frac{4}{12} =$ 6. $\frac{1}{5} + \frac{3}{5} =$

7. $\frac{8}{32} + \frac{18}{32} =$ 8. $\frac{3}{6} + \frac{3}{6} =$

9. $\frac{4}{16} + \frac{7}{16} =$ 10. $\frac{3}{14} + \frac{5}{14} =$

11. $\frac{11}{44} + \frac{11}{44} =$ 12. $\frac{3}{27} + \frac{4}{27} =$

13. $\frac{2}{9} + \frac{4}{9} =$ 14. $\frac{18}{48} + \frac{16}{48} =$

15. $\frac{4}{15} + \frac{3}{15} =$ 16. $\frac{8}{24} + \frac{4}{24} =$

17.   1/4 + 2/4 =   18.   3/12 + 4/12 =   19.   4/10 + 2/10 =

20.   1/3 + 2/3 =   21.   5/16 + 3/16 =   22.   3/8 + 3/8 =

23.   3/7 + 2/7 =   24.   6/32 + 8/32 =   25.   7/14 + 2/14 =

If I split a dollar into 100 pieces, I would have 100 pennies.

If I put 50 of those 100 pennies in my hand, I would be holding half of the dollar or "fifty one-hundredths." We write that fraction like this:

$$\frac{50}{100}$$

That fraction means I have 50 of the 100 pieces that it takes to make 1 whole dollar.

Now let's split that dollar into 4 pieces. That would be 4 quarters.

If I put 2 of those quarters in my hand, again I would be holding half of the dollar in my hand or "two fourths." We write that fraction like this:

$$\frac{2}{4}$$

That fraction means I have 2 of the 4 pieces that it takes to make 1 whole dollar.

I will split up that dollar one more time. This time I split it into 10 pieces.
We call those pieces dimes.

=   10

Again, I put half of the dollar into my hand. That means I have 5 of the 10
dimes in my hand. That fraction is "five tenths."

$$\frac{5}{10}$$

That fraction means I have 5 of the 10 pieces that it takes to make 1 whole
dollar. Let's take a closer look at those last 3 *equivalent* fractions. The
word *equivalent* means equal.

$$\frac{50}{100} \qquad \frac{2}{4} \qquad \frac{5}{10}$$

All three of those fractions are equal to one half. Since the number on top
is half of the number on bottom, they are all half. The first one is 50 of the
100 pennies, also known as half a dollar. The second fraction is 2 of the 4
quarters, or half a dollar. And the third fraction is 5 of the 10 dimes, also
half a dollar.

All those fractions equal one half. But there is a more simple way to write
one half. It is written as 1 of 2 pieces.

$$\frac{1}{2}$$

If I split a dollar into 2 fifty-cent pieces and I put one of them in my hand, I would be holding half a dollar. Looking at the fraction on the last page, I have 1 of the 2 pieces that it takes to make one whole dollar.

We have just learned 4 different ways to write one half.

$$\frac{1}{2} \qquad \frac{50}{100} \qquad \frac{2}{4} \qquad \frac{5}{10}$$

Here are 4 more ways to write one half.

$$\frac{3}{6} \qquad \frac{8}{16} \qquad \frac{100}{200} \qquad \frac{45}{90}$$

As long as the number on top is half of the number on bottom, it will always equal one half or $\frac{1}{2}$. Can you make up 4 more fractions that equal one half?

To do that, pick any number. Put that on the top of the fraction, then double that number and put it on the bottom of the fraction. You are sure to have a fraction that equals $\frac{1}{2}$. For example, these fractions all equal one half:

$$\frac{12}{24} \qquad \frac{11}{22} \qquad \frac{40}{80} \qquad \frac{4000}{8000}$$

Look at the first fraction and picture 2 dozen eggs; there are 24 total eggs. Half of the eggs would be 12, that's why $\frac{12}{24} = \frac{1}{2}$

Can you see why all of those fractions above equal $\frac{1}{2}$? If not, go back and read these lessons again. You must understand why those fractions equal $\frac{1}{2}$ before you move on.

Below are 4 statements. Find the one that is NOT true or not equal.

1.   1/2 = 5/10
2.   8/16 = 1/2
3.   3/4 = 1/2
4.   50/100 = ½

That's right, number 3 is not equal. 3/4 is more than 1/2.

Just to make sure you completely understand, let's try another example. Look at the sandwich below; it is one sandwich.

Cut the sandwich in half. I get half and you get half.

Even if you slice your half into two pieces, you still have 1/2 of the whole sandwich.

You could look at it as you have 2/4 (2 of the 4 pieces). No matter how many times you slice your half sandwich into smaller pieces, you still have only 1/2 of a sandwich.

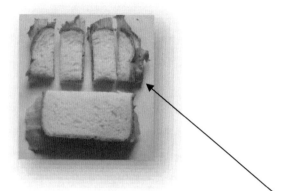

Here we have my half sandwich and your half. Your half is cut into 4 pieces. To write that as a fraction, I have 1/2 and you have 4/8. Do you understand how and why 1/2 equals 4/8? Look at the picture above. My half sandwich is "one of the two pieces" it takes to make one whole sandwich. Your half is "four of the eight *little* pieces" it would take to make one whole sandwich.

The number on the bottom of the fraction is called the *denominator*. You can remember that by thinking:

"The De-**bottom**-nator"

The number on top is called the *numerator* because it is the "number" of pieces we are talking about.

If this makes sense to you, complete the next worksheet. If you are confused, go back to where it was easy.

WORKSHEET 2-3

1. Circle the fraction that is equal to $\frac{1}{2}$.

$$\frac{4}{6} \qquad \frac{6}{6} \qquad \frac{3}{6} \qquad \frac{2}{6}$$

2. Which fraction is a bigger amount? Use a $<$ *or* $>$ sign.

$$\frac{9}{10} \qquad \frac{3}{10}$$

3. Write a math problem using fractions that means "four eighths plus three eighths" and then solve it.

4. I have a deck of cards. This deck has 52 cards. I want to separate the cards into 4 equal piles. Write a fraction that shows how much of the deck is in each pile.

5. I have one dozen eggs. One dozen is 12 eggs. I cooked 5 of the eggs. Write a fraction that shows how much of the dozen is left.

6. Look at the fraction below. Which number is the denominator?

$$\frac{3}{8}$$

7. Look at the fraction above. Which number is the numerator?

LESSON 4: COMMON DENOMINATORS

In Lesson 3, you learned about the sandwich pictured below. You learned that the half sandwich on top is sliced into eighths and there are 4 pieces, so the fraction is written $\frac{4}{8}$.

The half sandwich on the bottom is not sliced. It is one of the two pieces it takes to make one sandwich. That fraction is written $\frac{1}{2}$.

Next we will try to add up our two halves. We know it is going to equal one sandwich, but let's still look at the math.

$$\frac{1}{2} + \frac{4}{8} =$$

This isn't as simple as adding up the pennies, since the numbers on the bottom aren't the same. In order to add up our sandwich pieces, we are going to have to cut up my half sandwich into the same size pieces as your half. That way we get the two denominators to be the same.

The denominators need to be the same in order to add up the pieces. In math terms this is called a *common denominator*. Basically, the two fractions need to have something in *common*. So let's cut up my half sandwich into the same size pieces as your sandwich.

Now I have 4/8 of a sandwich too. The whole sandwich is now in 8 pieces. I have 4 of those pieces just like you. Here is the new math problem:

$$\frac{4}{8} + \frac{4}{8} = \frac{8}{8}$$

REMEMBER, we only add the numbers on the top; the numerators. The denominator, 8, is how many pieces there are all together in 1 whole sandwich.

ALSO REMEMBER, if the number on top and bottom are the same, it equals 1 because you have all the pieces that it takes to make one.

Having a sandwich to look at makes this problem seem somewhat simple. So let me tell you how to get a common denominator, when you don't have a sandwich to look at.

We will solve the same problem that we did above.

$$\frac{1}{2} + \frac{4}{8} =$$

Our two denominators are 2 and 8. We need them to be the same number. In order to turn a 2 into an 8, we have to multiply it by 4. We can do that, but if we multiply the denominator by 4, then we MUST multiply the numerator by 4 as well, so our fraction stays the same.

Here is how to turn 1/2 into 4/8. Multiply both numbers by 4.

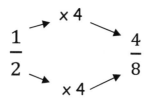

Now that we have turned 1/2 into 4/8, we can add our sandwich fractions together.

$$\frac{4}{8} + \frac{4}{8} = \frac{8}{8}$$

Remember, do not add the denominators together; that would mess up our sandwich pieces. Just add the two numerators together and, of course, we end up with one whole sandwich.

Let's try another one without any sandwich pictures. We'll go through the steps to get a common denominator. Here's the problem:

$$\frac{1}{2} + \frac{3}{10} =$$

Our two denominators are 2 and 10. We need them to be the same. What will it take to turn a 2 into a 10? We can multiply it by 5 and that will equal 10. BUT REMEMBER, whatever you do to the denominator you MUST do to the numerator. Multiply both by 5 to keep our fraction the same size. Here is the math.

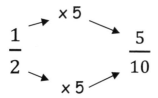

We just turned $\frac{1}{2}$ into $\frac{5}{10}$. Now it is easy to add those fractions together. Just add the numerators.

New fraction for one half

$$\frac{5}{10} + \frac{3}{10} =$$

The denominators are the same, so just add the two numerators. The answer is $\frac{8}{10}$.

Let's try a more difficult problem.

$$\frac{9}{77} + \frac{7}{11} =$$

Our first step is to get two common denominators. How can we turn 11 into 77? Multiply by 7! Next, we MUST multiply the numerator by 7 as well. So now we have turned 7/11 into 49/77 by multiplying both the numerator and denominator by 7. Now we can do the math.

$$\frac{9}{77} + \frac{49}{77} =$$

Add up the numerators and the answer is 58/77.

Take a look at this next problem. Try to find a common denominator.

$$\frac{3}{8} + \frac{1}{3} =$$

This one is tricky because there is no number that will turn a 3 into an 8. When this happens, just multiply the two denominators together to find a common denominator. Multiply 8 x 3. The answer, 24, will be our common denominator.

When you change both denominators, you MUST change both numerators too. I have given both our fractions a new common denominator. Next we need to get two new numerators.

$$\frac{3}{8} + \frac{1}{3} = \qquad \frac{}{24} + \frac{}{24} =$$

We multiplied 8 x 3 to get 24, so we need to multiply the numerator by **3** as well. The math is 3 x 3 = 9. That's the new numerator.

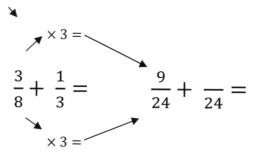

$$\frac{3}{8} + \frac{1}{3} = \qquad \frac{9}{24} + \frac{}{24} =$$

Can you figure out the missing numerator above? What did we do to the denominator to get 24? That's right, we multiplied it by 8. Do the same thing to the numerator to get the answer.

$$\frac{3}{8} + \frac{1}{3} = \qquad \frac{9}{24} + \frac{8}{24} =$$

Now we are ready to add our two new fractions together.

$$\frac{9}{24} + \frac{8}{24} = \frac{17}{24}$$

26

Let's try one more together.

$$\frac{2}{5} + \frac{1}{6} =$$

There is no number that will turn 5 into 6, so we will have to multiply them together. Multiplying the two denominators automatically gives us a common denominator, 5 x 6 = 30.

$$\frac{2}{5} + \frac{1}{6} = \qquad\qquad \frac{}{30} + \frac{}{30} =$$

This denominator was multiplied by 6 to get a common denominator, so do the same thing to the numerator. 6 x 2 = 12.

$$\frac{2}{5} + \frac{1}{6} = \qquad\qquad \frac{12}{30} + \frac{?}{30} =$$

Can you figure out the missing numerator? We multiplied this number by 5 to get our common denominator, so do the same to the numerator. 1 x 5 = 5.

$$\frac{2}{5} + \frac{1}{6} = \qquad 1\times5 \qquad \frac{12}{30} + \frac{5}{30} =$$
$$6\times5$$

Now we are ready to add our fractions. Just add the numerators.

$$\frac{12}{30} + \frac{5}{30} = \frac{17}{30}$$

Complete the next worksheet. You will need to get common denominators and then add the numerators. If you don't get 100% correct on this worksheet, read this lesson again. You shouldn't move to the next lesson until this is easy math!

WORKSHEET 2-4

1. $\frac{2}{5} + \frac{3}{10} =$

2. $\frac{3}{8} + \frac{3}{24} =$

3. $\frac{5}{12} + \frac{3}{6} =$

4. $\frac{2}{4} + \frac{3}{8} =$

5. $\frac{5}{22} + \frac{1}{11} =$

6. $\frac{8}{14} + \frac{1}{7} =$

7. $\frac{2}{3} + \frac{1}{4} =$

8. $\frac{1}{5} + \frac{1}{2} =$

9. $\frac{1}{4} + \frac{7}{16} =$

10. $\frac{2}{7} + \frac{2}{3} =$

11. In January, Josh grew three eighths of an inch. In February he grew one fourth of an inch. How much did he grow all together in those two months?

12. Write and solve a math problem using fractions to add one dime and seven pennies.

13. Carrie ate five eighths of the pizza. Anita ate six sixteenths of the pizza. Is there any pizza left?

14. Which fraction is bigger? Use a $<$ or $>$ sign. $\frac{2}{100}$ $\frac{7}{8}$

I want to add the two fractions below. I will need to find a common denominator first.

$$\frac{3}{8} + \frac{1}{6} =$$

You could multiply the two denominators together, but 48 is such a big number, there must be something smaller. Can you think of another number that both 8 and 6 can go into evenly? Let's see...6 x 2 is 12, that won't work. And 6 x 3 = 18, that won't work either. But 6 x 4 = 24! That WILL work because 8 goes into 24 evenly too, 8 x 3 = 24. Let's use 24 as our common denominator.

$$\frac{3}{8} + \frac{1}{6} = \qquad \frac{}{24} + \frac{}{24}$$

Now we need numerators, this fraction first. How did we turn 8 into 24? We multiplied it by 3, right? Do the same thing to the numerator.

$$\frac{3}{8} + \frac{1}{6} = \qquad \overset{\times 3}{\frac{9}{24}} + \frac{}{24}$$

How did we turn 6 into 24? We multiplied by 4, right? Do the same thing to the numerator.

$$\frac{3}{8} + \frac{1}{6} = \qquad \overset{\times 4}{\frac{9}{24}} + \frac{4}{24}$$

Now we are ready to add the fractions.

$$\frac{9}{24} + \frac{4}{24} = \frac{13}{24}$$

Do you understand WHY we need to have common denominators before adding fractions? Because whether we are adding sandwich pieces or money we need all the pieces to be the same size before we can add them up.

Let's try another one together.

$$\frac{1}{4} + \frac{1}{6} =$$

Can you think of a number that both 4 and 6 will go into evenly? Here is one way to figure that out. Below are two rows of numbers. On top, I am counting by 4's. On the lower row, I am counting by 6's. As soon as I find the same number in both rows, I will have my denominator!

$$4...8...12...16...20..$$
$$6...12...18...24$$

When I list numbers like that, I am writing the *multiples* of 4 and the *multiples* of 6. Look for the first number that they both have in common.

$$4...8...12...16...20$$
$$6...12...18...24$$

The number 12 is the first number to show up in both sets of multiples, so it is called a *common multiple* of 4 and 6. If I kept the list going on and on, we would see other common multiples of 4 and 6. For example 24 is a common multiple and so is 36. But the number 12 is the LEAST (smallest) common multiple of 4 and 6, so that's what we'll use for our denominator.

$$\frac{1}{4} + \frac{1}{6} = \frac{}{12} + \frac{}{12}$$

Can you fill in the numerators? Think to yourself...how did I turn a 4 into a 12? You multiplied it by 3, so do the same thing to the numerator above the 4.

$$\frac{1}{4} + \frac{1}{6} = \quad \frac{3}{12} + \frac{}{12}$$

Can you fill in the missing numerator above? Think to yourself...how did I turn a 6 into a 12? You multiplied it by 2. Do the same thing to the numerator and then add the fractions.

$$\frac{1}{4} + \frac{1}{6} = \quad \frac{3}{12} + \frac{2}{12} = \frac{5}{12}$$

The term *Least Common Multiple* is used a lot in math, so let's take a closer look at that phrase. The first word, "Least" means the smallest. The opposite of "Least" is "Greatest." Greatest means the biggest number and "Least" means the smallest number.

The second word in "Least Common Multiple" is "Common." If you and your friend both have blue eyes, then that is something you have in common. If you both have the same first name, then that is something else you have in common. The word "common" means two things are alike.

The last word in "Least Common Multiple" is "Multiple." When we multiply a number, we get multiples of that number. For example, here is a list of multiples of 9.

$9 \times 1 \quad 9 \times 2 \quad 9 \times 3 \quad 9 \times 4 \quad 9 \times 5 \quad 9 \times 6$

9...18...27...36...45...54

And here is a list of multiples of 6:

6...12...18...24...30...36...42

The "Least Common Multiple" is the smallest number that both sets of multiples have in common. So, what is the Least Common Multiple of 6 and 9?

18

Now try to add these fractions together on your own. Find the Least Common Multiple (LCM) of 9 and 12 to help you find a common denominator.

$$\frac{5}{12} + \frac{1}{9} =$$

Start by counting by 9's, to get a list of multiples of 9. Next, count by 12's until you find a common multiple. Choose the smallest one or the LCM (Least Common Multiple).

9...18...27...36...45...54...63...72
12...24...36...48...60...72

Do you see any common multiples? Choose the smallest common number to use as your denominator.

$$\frac{5}{12} + \frac{1}{9} = \qquad \frac{15}{36} + \frac{4}{36} = \frac{19}{36}$$

Think you've got it? Then complete the next worksheet.

Name_____Date_____

WORKSHEET 2-4.5

1. $\dfrac{4}{9} + \dfrac{2}{6} =$

2. $\dfrac{1}{6} + \dfrac{4}{8} =$

3. $\dfrac{1}{4} + \dfrac{5}{8} =$

4. $\dfrac{5}{12} + \dfrac{3}{8} =$

5. $\dfrac{2}{3} + \dfrac{1}{6} =$

6. $\dfrac{3}{14} + \dfrac{3}{4} =$

7. Beth ate $\dfrac{3}{8}$ of the pizza and Chris ate $\dfrac{3}{5}$ of it. Is there any pizza left?

LESSON 5: REDUCING FRACTIONS

Let's take another look at some fractions that all equal one half.

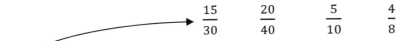

$$\frac{15}{30} \qquad \frac{20}{40} \qquad \frac{5}{10} \qquad \frac{4}{8}$$

You'll notice that each of the fractions above, describe $\frac{1}{2}$ of something. The first one is 15 of the 30 pieces needed, to make 1 whole something. The second one is 20 of the 40 pieces. The third fraction is 5 of the 10 pieces needed to make 1. And the last fraction is 4 of the 8 pieces. Anytime the numerator is one half of the denominator, the fraction is equal to $\frac{1}{2}$.

For our first example, we are going to use the fraction below.

$$\frac{3}{6}$$

We know this is the same thing as $\frac{1}{2}$ because if we sliced our sandwich into 6 pieces, and I gave you 3 of the 6 pieces, you would have half and so would I. But you normally wouldn't say three sixths of a sandwich; you would say one half. To change a fraction from $\frac{3}{6}$ to $\frac{1}{2}$ is called *reducing*. Let me explain.

Reducing a fraction is a lot like finding a common denominator, only it's the opposite process. For example, look at the fraction below.

$$\frac{3}{6}$$

To reduce 3/6, we need to find a number that both the 3 and the 6 are divisible by. That is, find a number that can divide both numbers evenly with no remainders. We can divide both the numerator and denominator by 3 without any remainders. Let's try that.

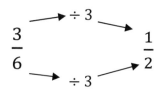

That's how to reduce fractions. *Divide* both the numerator and denominator, by the same number.

Let's try another one. We want to reduce the following fraction.

$$\frac{8}{24}$$

Can you think of a number that can divide both 8 and 24 evenly? They can both be divided by 2. That would reduce it down to 4/12, but we can reduce further than that. Look at 8 and 24 again. Can you think of a number bigger than 2 that can divide both 8 and 24 evenly? How about 4? That will work, but there is still one number even bigger...how about 8? Divide both 8 and 24 by 8 and our fraction reduces down to 1/3.

If you had divided by the smallest number 2, instead of 8, you would have got 4/12. Then if you divided that by 2 again, it would reduce down to 2/6. Then, you would have divided those by 2 one more time and eventually you would have gotten down to 1/3; just like we did above, when we divided by 8.

Starting with the biggest number possible saves you steps, but either way you get the same answer - eventually.

It is called "reducing down to the smallest denominator possible" when you divide as far as possible. Let's try one more together. Can you reduce this fraction down to the smallest denominator possible?

$$\frac{9}{36}$$

What number can we use to divide both of these numbers evenly? Let's start by dividing them both by 3.

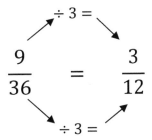

$$\frac{9}{36} = \frac{3}{12}$$

Dividing the numerator and denominator by 3, reduces our fraction down to $\frac{3}{12}$, but that is not the smallest possible denominator. We can divide each of *those* numbers by 3, too.

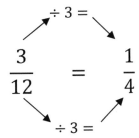

$$\frac{3}{12} = \frac{1}{4}$$

There we go. Now our fraction is reduced down to the smallest denominator possible.

Are you ready to complete the next worksheet on your own? If this is difficult for you, go back and read this lesson again.

WORKSHEET 2-5

Reduce the following fractions down to the smallest denominator possible.

1. $\dfrac{3}{21}$ $=$ $—$

   $\div 3 =$

   $\div 3 =$

2. $\dfrac{4}{12}$ $=$ $—$

   $\div ? =$

   $\div ? =$

3. $\dfrac{3}{9}$ $=$ $—$

4. $\dfrac{50}{100} =$

5. $\dfrac{5}{25} =$

6. $\dfrac{28}{49} =$

In the last lesson, you learned how to reduce fractions. You were told to divide each number in the fraction, by the same number, until you couldn't divide any further. Look at the fraction below.

$$\frac{4}{12} = \frac{1}{3}$$

I divided each number by 4, to reduce it down to $\frac{1}{3}$. But there is another way. If you really like math, you might enjoy this lesson. But if you don't care for math, you may find this lesson a little annoying. This is one of those things in math that you won't use much in life, but it comes up on tests all the time, so you must be aware of the *Greatest Common Factor*.

Let's take a closer look at that phrase, *Greatest Common Factor*. The first word, "Greatest" means the biggest number. The second word, "Common" means to share something the same and the last word is "Factor." Do you remember what a factor is? Look at the problem below.

$$3 \times 5 = 15$$

Factors are the numbers being multiplied. In the problem above, 3 and 5 are factors of 15. So the phrase *Greatest Common Factor* means the biggest factor that two numbers share. Sometimes it is just called the GCF. Let me explain. Let's say you want to reduce this fraction.

$$\frac{72}{144}$$

We could divide by 2 until we get all the way down to the smallest denominator possible, but that will be a lot of dividing. The best choice would be to divide by the biggest, or greatest, number possible. You can find the Greatest Factor that these two numbers have in common by listing all their factors.

$$\text{Factors of } 72 \quad 1, 2, 3, 4, 6, 8, 9, 12, 18, 24, 36, 72$$

$$\text{Factors of } 144 \quad 1, 2, 3, 4, 6, 8, 12, 16, 18, 24, 36, 48, 72, 144$$

Looking at the two lists above, you can see that 72 and 144 have a lot of common factors. But we are looking for the GREATEST common factor, that is, the BIGGEST number that both numbers are divisible by.

$$\text{Factors of } 72 \quad 1, 2, 3, 4, 6, 8, 9, 12, 18, 24, 36, \boxed{72}$$

$$\text{Factors of } 144 \quad 1, 2, 3, 4, 6, 8, 12, 16, 18, 24, 36, 48, \boxed{72,} 144$$

It looks like 72 is the Greatest Common Factor of 72 and 144. Let's go back to the fraction we were trying to reduce.

$$\frac{72}{144}$$

Since the Greatest Common Factor is 72, that is the best number to divide with, to reduce that fraction.

$$\frac{72}{144} = \frac{1}{2}$$

You might be thinking that this sounds a lot like the "Least Common Multiple." You are right, except that the GCF is kind of the opposite of LCM. One is looking for the biggest factor and the other is looking for the smallest multiple.

Look at it this way; when you are trying to find the Least Common MULTIPLE of two numbers, you will be MULTIPLYING those numbers. And when you are finding the Greatest Common FACTOR, you will be DIVIDING, to get down to the factors. Does that make sense? Follow the arrows below to see the difference between factors of 72 and multiples of 72.

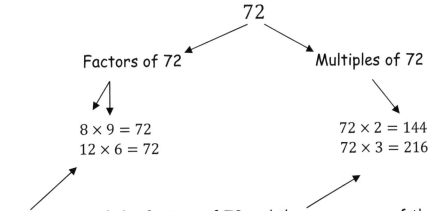

These are some of the factors of 72 and these are some of the multiples of 72.

Make sure you understand what it means to find the Greatest Common Factor (GCF) and the Least Common Multiple (LCM) because it WILL be on a math test someday. But it's not as complicated as it sounds. Just look at the words in each phrase to figure it out.

Keep in mind that you will never be asked to find the GREATEST common MULTIPLE because that would be one huge number. And you will never be asked to find the LEAST common FACTOR because that will always be 1. Every number has 1 as a factor, so that would always be the least common factor. Your job is to understand how to find the Greatest Common Factor (GCF) and the Least Common Multiple (LCM).

On the next worksheet, you will be asked to reduce your answers. If finding the GCF helps you, use that method to reduce. Otherwise, use your own method. Just make sure you know what the Greatest Common Factor is and how to find the GCF of two numbers.

Name _____ Date_____

Worksheet 2-5.5

Add the following fractions. Reduce your answers down to the smallest denominator possible.

1. $\frac{2}{12} + \frac{2}{60} =$

2. $\frac{2}{8} + \frac{4}{6} =$

3. $\frac{7}{25} + \frac{4}{75} =$

4. $\frac{3}{48} + \frac{51}{144} =$

5. $\frac{2}{11} + \frac{11}{121} =$

6. List all the factors of 64 and 72 and then circle the Greatest Common Factors.

   64 __ __ __ __ __ __ __

   72 __ __ __ __ __ __ __ __ __ __ __ __

7. List 10 multiples of 6 and 8 and then circle the Least Common Multiple.

   6   __ __ __ __ __ __ __ __ __ __

   8   __ __ __ __ __ __ __ __ __ __

LESSON 6: READING FRACTIONS ON A RULER

During your life you will need to know fractions for a variety of different reasons, but the most common reason is to be able to read a ruler or tape measure. Here is how to apply your new knowledge of fractions to a ruler. The symbol for inches is a quotation mark, as in 8" - that means 8 inches.

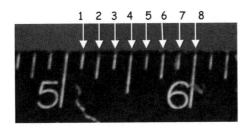

Above is a section of a ruler showing inch number 5 divided into 8 pieces. Each piece is $\frac{1}{8}$ of an inch. Look at the ruler and try to figure out why the lines between the 5 and 6 are different lengths. Notice the lines next to the 5 and 6 are the longest. Half way in between is the next longest line. It stands for $\frac{1}{2}$ inch. Shorter lines are used, to split the $\frac{1}{2}$ inch into a couple of $\frac{1}{4}$ inch pieces. And the shortest lines represent $\frac{1}{8}$ inch.

If that is not absolutely clear to you, read the last paragraph again. You must completely understand every line on the ruler pictured above, before you can move forward. Think of each line as a different denominator. The shortest line has a denominator of 8 and the longest line has a denominator of 2.

The ruler on the next page slices an inch into 16 equal pieces. How would you write a fraction for one of those 16 pieces?

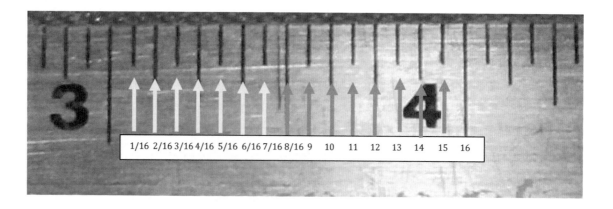

You should have guessed $\frac{1}{16}$ of an inch. If an inch is cut up into 16 pieces, then of course, 1 piece would be $\frac{1}{16}$.

Look at the ruler below and try to find the line for $5\frac{3}{8}$".

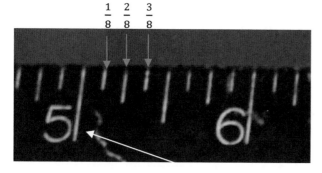

Start at the long line next to the 5. Move over one line to $5\frac{1}{8}$". The next line, which is a little longer, marks $\frac{1}{4}$". If you move over one more line, you are at $5\frac{3}{8}$". Do you understand why I called the $\frac{2}{8}$ mark $\frac{1}{4}$"? They are the same amount, one is just reduced.

Where is the big arrow pointing?

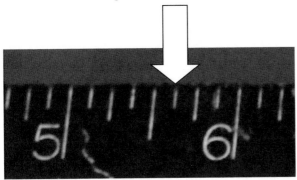

You know the long line in the center is $\frac{1}{2}$" and each little piece is another $\frac{1}{8}$",

so let's add them together.

$$\frac{1}{2} + \frac{1}{8} =$$

Find a common denominator. We will use 8.

$$\frac{1}{2} \text{ turns into } \frac{4}{8} =$$

So the new problem looks like this:

$$\frac{4}{8} + \frac{1}{8} = \frac{5}{8}$$

The arrow is pointing to $5\frac{5}{8}$".

Look at the ruler on the next page. Each inch is sliced into 16 pieces. How would you write a fraction to represent where the big arrow is pointing?

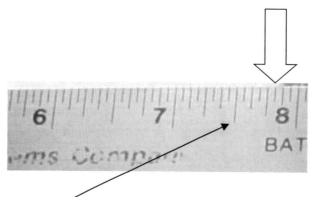

First find the $\frac{1}{2}$" mark. This ruler divides each inch into 16 pieces, so $\frac{1}{2}$" is equal to $\frac{8}{16}$" because 8 is half of 16. So start at the $\frac{1}{2}$" mark, then count how many 16ths there are after $\frac{1}{2}$". I count 5. There are $\frac{5}{16}$ after the $\frac{1}{2}$". Let's do the math.

We know $\frac{1}{2}$" = $\frac{8}{16}$", so the new problem is:

$$\frac{8}{16} + \frac{5}{16} = \frac{13}{16}$$

The arrow on the ruler is pointing to $7\frac{13}{16}$".

Can you figure out the smallest measurement on this next ruler?

The first inch on this ruler is sliced up more than the second inch. Since the 16ths have been split in half, we now have 32 pieces. The smallest measurement on this ruler is 1/32 and it is pronounced "one thirty-second."

WORKSHEET 2-6

Find each measurement.

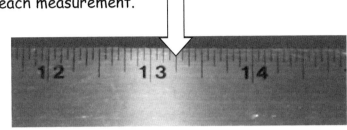

1.

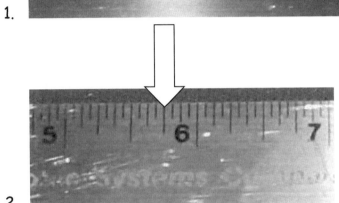

2.

3.

4.

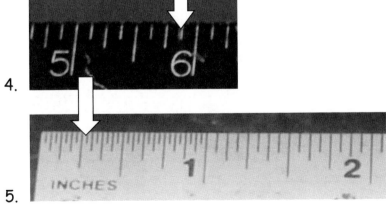

5.

LESSON 7: SUBTRACTING FRACTIONS

Now that you have successfully added fractions, reduced fractions, and found a common denominator, let's try subtracting fractions. We'll start off simple with fractions that already have a common denominator.

As you look at these problems, realize that all you really need to do is subtract the numerators. Let's do one together first. Here is the problem.

$$\frac{5}{10} - \frac{3}{10} =$$

First of all, we know the answer is going to have a denominator of 10, so let's just write that down first.

$$\frac{5}{10} - \frac{3}{10} = \frac{}{10}$$

Next, we just subtract the numerators. 5 – 3 = 2, so the answer is...

$$\frac{5}{10} - \frac{3}{10} = \frac{2}{10} \quad reduces\ to \quad \frac{1}{5}$$

with $2 \div 2$ and $10 \div 2$

Since both 2 and 10 can be divided evenly by 2, $\frac{2}{10}$ reduces down to $\frac{1}{5}$.

Here is another one.

$$\frac{7}{8} - \frac{7}{16} =$$

First, you need a common denominator. How can you turn 8 into 16? Multiply by 2. Do the same thing to the numerator. Now can you solve this problem?

$$\frac{14}{16} - \frac{7}{16} =$$

Complete the next worksheet.

Name: _____   Date: _____

WORKSHEET 2-7

Subtract the following fractions. If the denominators aren't the same, find a common denominator. Make sure to reduce each of your answers down to the smallest denominator possible.

1. $\dfrac{8}{24} - \dfrac{2}{24} =$ 2. $\dfrac{9}{36} - \dfrac{3}{36} =$

3. $\dfrac{5}{8} - \dfrac{3}{8} =$ 4. $\dfrac{10}{16} - \dfrac{2}{16} =$

5. $\dfrac{12}{32} - \dfrac{4}{32} =$ 6. $\dfrac{9}{45} - \dfrac{4}{45} =$

7. $\dfrac{8}{10} - \dfrac{1}{3} =$ 8. $\dfrac{3}{4} - \dfrac{1}{5} =$

9. $\dfrac{2}{3} - \dfrac{2}{7} =$ 10. $\dfrac{15}{16} - \dfrac{3}{4} =$

11.   I drew a line with a big marker. The line was $\dfrac{1}{4}$ inch wide. I drew another line next to it; making it twice as thick. How thick is the line now?

12.   We planted grass two weeks ago. On Monday, the grass was $\dfrac{3}{8}$ inches tall. The following Monday, it measured $\dfrac{15}{16}$ inches tall. How much did the grass grow during that week?

Look at the fraction below. Both the numerator and the denominator have a zero at the end.

$$\frac{10}{50}$$

Whenever you see this situation, you can quickly reduce by crossing out the zeros.

$$\frac{1\cancel{0}}{5\cancel{0}} = \frac{1}{5}$$

However, make sure you cross off the same amount of zeros from the top as you do from the bottom. Can you reduce this fraction?

$$\frac{7,000}{16,000,000}$$

Just cross out the same amount of zeros from the numerator as the denominator. This is what you are left with.

$$\frac{7,\cancel{000}}{16,000,\cancel{000}} = \frac{7}{16,000}$$

Here is another quick trick to reducing fractions. If both the numerator and denominator are even numbers, you can always divide by 2.

$$\frac{48}{100}$$

Both 48 and 100 are even numbers, so start reducing by dividing them both by 2.

$$\frac{48}{100} = \frac{24}{50}$$

with $\div 2 =$ shown above and below the arrows

But wait! 24 and 50 are also even numbers, so let's divide each number by 2 again.

$$\frac{48}{100} = \frac{24}{50} = \frac{12}{25}$$

with $\div 2 =$ shown above and below the arrows

There is no number that goes into both 12 and 25 evenly, so we are finished reducing. The fraction above is reduced down to the smallest denominator possible.

You already know that each of the following fractions equal 1.

$$\frac{4}{4} \qquad \frac{2}{2} \qquad \frac{10}{10}$$

This fraction means you have all 4 of the 4 pieces you need to make 1. The second fraction means you have both of the halves you need to make 1. And the last fraction means something was sliced into 10 pieces and you have all 10 pieces. In other words, you have 1.

Now look at these fractions. Can you figure out how much each fraction equals?

$$\frac{10}{1} \qquad \frac{8}{1} \qquad \frac{7}{1}$$

When the denominator is 1; that means it takes 1 piece to make 1. In the first fraction the numerator is 10, so you have 10 of those pieces. In other words, you have 10. Look at the second fraction. You have 8 pieces. It takes 1 of those pieces to make 1. You have 8 of them.

$$\frac{10}{1} = 10 \qquad \frac{8}{1} = 8 \qquad \frac{7}{1} =$$

Can you answer the last problem? Since the denominator is 1, the answer is 7.

You can also turn any whole number into a fraction, by giving it a denominator of 1. For example, to turn 3 into a fraction, write it like this:

$$3 = \frac{3}{1}$$

Another tip: When you look at the three fractions below, think money.

$$\frac{1}{4} \qquad \frac{1}{2} \qquad \frac{3}{4}$$

One quarter $= \frac{1}{4} =$ = one quarter of a dollar

One half $= \frac{1}{2} = \frac{2}{4} =$ = one half of a dollar

Three quarters $= \frac{3}{4} =$ = three quarters of a dollar

With that information, try to solve these next problems in your head without getting a common denominator first. ~ Think money.

$$\frac{1}{2} + \frac{1}{4} = \qquad\qquad \frac{3}{4} - \frac{1}{2} = \qquad\qquad \frac{10}{20} + \frac{10}{40} =$$

Did you look at the first problem has 2 quarters plus 1 quarter? Did you look at the second problem as 75 cents minus 50 cents? Did you cross out the zeros on the last problem and look at it as a half dollar plus a quarter? That's how I want you to look at those fractions. Think money.

Let's say you cut up a stick of butter (or margarine) into 4 equal pieces. Each piece would be $\frac{1}{4}$ of a stick of butter. One fourth stick of butter means it is one of the four pieces needed to make one stick of butter.

Now let's say you cut up a stick of butter into 20 equal pieces. Each piece would be $\frac{1}{20}$ of a cube of butter. Take a look at those two fractions below.

$$\frac{1}{4} \quad or \quad \frac{1}{20}$$

Can you tell me which fraction is bigger? The rule to be learned here is when the numerators are the same, the one with the bigger denominator, is the smaller fraction. Look at the next two fractions. Which fraction is bigger?

$$\frac{2}{100} \quad or \quad \frac{2}{10}$$

Do you want 2 slices of a candy bar that has been sliced into 100 pieces? Or would you rather have 2 slices of a candy bar that has been sliced into 10 pieces? If you still don't know which fraction is bigger, go back to the last lesson you understood.

This new rule is only true, however, if the numerators are the same. When the numerators are different, you have to look at them logically. Look at the two fractions below. Which one is bigger?

$$\frac{75}{100} \quad or \quad \frac{2}{10}$$

This time the fraction with the bigger denominator is bigger than the other fraction. Do you understand why? There are several ways to figure out which one is the bigger fraction.

First, you could have looked at each fraction as money. The first fraction, $\frac{75}{100}$, is the same as 75 pennies, or 75 cents. The second fraction, $\frac{2}{10}$, is the same as 2 dimes or 20 cents. Now can you tell which one is bigger?

The second way to solve that problem is to get a common denominator and see which one has the bigger numerator. A good common denominator to use would be 100. Turn the 10 into 100.

$$\frac{75}{100} \qquad \frac{2}{10}$$

Multiply 10 x 10 to get 100. And remember, whatever you do to the denominator you must do to the numerator. Multiply 2 x 10 and write the new fractions.

$$\frac{75}{100} \qquad \frac{20}{100}$$

Now can you tell which fraction is bigger, $\frac{75}{100}$ or $\frac{20}{100}$? The first fraction means we have 75 of the pieces. The second fraction means we have 20 of the pieces. You must know which one is bigger by now!

One last final way is to cross multiply. It is the craziest little math trick, but it works. Let me explain. We will use the same two fractions we used above.

$$\frac{75}{100} \qquad \frac{2}{10}$$

To find out which fraction is bigger, multiply in the direction of the arrows.

$$\frac{75}{100} \qquad \frac{2}{10}$$

The math is: 100 x 2 = 200   10 x 75 = 750.

Put your answers above the numerator you multiplied.

The biggest answer is the biggest fraction.

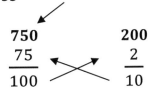

$$\frac{75}{100} \qquad \frac{2}{10}$$

Complete the next worksheet.

Name: _____   Date: _____

WORKSHEET 2-8

Solve the following problems. Reduce your answer to the smallest denominator possible.

1. $\frac{1}{5} + \frac{2}{10} =$

2. $\frac{3}{6} + \frac{4}{8} =$

3. $\frac{1}{4} + \frac{6}{8} =$

4. $\frac{2}{4} + \frac{1}{7} =$

5. $\frac{5}{6} - \frac{20}{120} =$

6. $\frac{3}{4} - \frac{1}{2} =$

7. $\frac{4}{7} - \frac{2}{8} =$

8. $\frac{30}{60} - \frac{20}{40} =$

9. Tina is making some cookies. The recipe calls for one half cup of sugar. She only has one quarter cup of sugar. How much more sugar does she need to make the cookies?

10. Carrie was trying to find one dozen colored eggs. One dozen equals 12 eggs. So far she has found 9 of them. Write a fraction that shows how much of the dozen she has left to find.

Cross multiply and then use a $<$ or $>$ sign to say which fraction is bigger.

11. $\frac{5}{8}$ $\frac{7}{12}$

12. $\frac{7}{9}$ $\frac{6}{7}$

13. $\frac{3}{4}$ $\frac{6}{8}$

LESSON 9: MULTIPLYING AND DIVIDING FRACTION

Good News! Multiplying and dividing fractions is easy. First, multiplication - it couldn't be simpler. Just multiply straight across, numerators and denominators.

$$\frac{3}{4} \times \frac{6}{10} = \frac{18}{40}$$

That's it! Just multiply the two numerators and then multiply the two denominators.

Try one yourself. Multiply the numerators together. Put your answer here.

$$\frac{3}{4} \times \frac{4}{7} = -$$

Then just multiply the two denominators together. Put that answer there. You don't have to worry about getting a common denominator; that is just for addition and subtraction.

Next you will learn how to divide fractions. This is a funny one. To divide fractions you have to *flip* over the second fraction. Look at this problem.

$$\frac{4}{8} \div \frac{1}{2} =$$

Start by *flipping* the second fraction. Now instead of $\frac{1}{2}$, you'll write $\frac{2}{1}$. When you flip a fraction like this, it is called the *reciprocal* (re-sip-ra-coal).

Below are five fractions. Flip them over to get the reciprocal of each fraction.

$$\frac{5}{9} \qquad \frac{3}{4} \qquad \frac{1}{2} \qquad \frac{2}{5} \qquad \frac{3}{10}$$

Pretty simple, huh? That is just the first step to dividing fractions.
After you flip the second fraction and get the reciprocal, you multiply
straight across - that's right, MULTIPLY!

Dividing fractions is funny because you never actually do any division. You
just flip the second fraction and then multiply the numerators and the
denominators.

$$\frac{4}{8} \times \frac{2}{1} = \frac{8}{8} \; or \; 1$$

It is hard to explain why this works, but I can show you a couple problems
that might help you understand.

When you want to find half of any number, you can do one of two things. You
can multiply the number by $\frac{1}{2}$ or you can divide the number by 2. Let's use an
example whose answer you already know. Do you know how much is half of 4?
Half of 4 is 2, right? Here is the math to prove that half of 4 is 2. The
math is four times one half.

$$\frac{4}{1} \times \frac{1}{2} = \frac{4}{2} = 2$$

$\frac{4}{2}$ reduces down to 2

Now let's prove that half of four is two, by *dividing with fractions*. I have
written out the math below to divide four, by two – in fraction form. To
divide fractions, start by getting the reciprocal of the second fraction.

$$\frac{4}{1} \div \frac{2}{1} =$$

Once you get the reciprocal, turn it into a multiplication problem.

$$\frac{4}{1} \times \frac{1}{2} =$$

But wait! That's the same thing as multiplying by one half! That's what we did the first time, we multiplied by one half. Mmm...interesting. Does that help you see how and why getting the reciprocal and then multiplying works?

Well... either way, all you need to know is how to multiply and divide fractions. I'll say it one more time. To divide fractions, get the reciprocal of the second fraction and then multiply straight across. If you understand all that, complete the next worksheet.

WORKSHEET 2-9

Multiply or divide the following fractions. Be sure to reduce your answer.

1. $\dfrac{4}{8} \times \dfrac{2}{1} =$

2. $\dfrac{4}{8} \div \dfrac{2}{1} =$

3. $\dfrac{1}{10} \times \dfrac{5}{1} =$

4. $\dfrac{1}{4} \div \dfrac{2}{3} =$

5. $\dfrac{3}{4} \times \dfrac{3}{7} =$

6. $\dfrac{2}{6} \div \dfrac{4}{5} =$

7. I stacked up 4 pieces of wood. Each piece is $\dfrac{1}{8}$ inch thick. How tall is the stack of wood? (one eighth times four)

8. Divide two fifths by three fourth.

9. Multiply. $\dfrac{3}{5} \times \dfrac{1}{4} =$

   Next, divide your answer by $\dfrac{1}{4}$.

   Reduce your answer. The new answer should be $\dfrac{3}{5}$.

To find half of any number, multiply it by $\dfrac{1}{2}$ or divide by 2.

10. How much is one half of $\dfrac{3}{4}$?

11. How much is one half of $\dfrac{7}{8}$?

12. Write and solve a math problem using fractions to prove that one half of two is one.

LESSON 10: IMPROPER FRACTIONS AND MIXED NUMBERS

OK...you understand fractions, right? You know that a fraction is a piece of something. It is less than one, but more than zero. The denominator is how many pieces it takes to make one and the numerator is how many pieces we are talking about. You also know that the fraction below equals one.

$$\frac{4}{4} = 1$$

But wait! A fraction equal to one? How can that be? I thought a fraction was less than one. The "fraction" above isn't really a fraction of a number, it is a whole number written as a fraction. You can write any number as a fraction. For example, here is the number 4 written as a fraction.

$$\frac{4}{1} = 4$$

Once a fraction becomes more than 1, it is called an *Improper Fraction*. For example, the fraction below is an *improper fraction*. The numerator is larger than the denominator, which makes it more than one.

$$\frac{5}{4}$$

The fraction above is read, five quarters or five fourths. Look at the fraction above as if it were money. You already know that four quarters $\left(\frac{4}{4}\right)$ equal one dollar. So how much is five quarters?

61

$$\frac{5}{4} = \$1.25 = one\ and\ one\ quarter = 1\ \frac{1}{4}$$

Do you see how $\frac{5}{4}$ is the same as $1\frac{1}{4}$?

An improper fraction is improper because it is more than 1. A fraction is less than 1, so when the numerator is bigger than the denominator, it is improper.

Here is another approach to understanding improper fractions.

If 1 full deck of cards has 52 cards, then we can safely say that just 3 of those cards would be 3/52 of the whole deck.

Half of the deck of cards would be 26/52, which of course we can reduce down. (Divide both numbers by 26 and you get 1/2).

If we added 4 aces from another deck, to our deck of cards, we would have 56 cards total. Write that number as an improper fraction.

$$\frac{56}{52}$$

That is an *improper fraction* because it is more than one. The numerator is larger than the denominator. To reduce it down, so it isn't improper, take away 52 of the 56 cards, and call that 1 deck. We are left with 4 extra cards. They are written as 4/52.

$$\frac{56}{52} = 1\ \frac{4}{52}$$

Look at that answer again, $1\frac{4}{52}$. The numerator and denominator are both even numbers. That means we can reduce it down by dividing each number by 2. The answer is now:

$$1\frac{2}{26}$$

But wait! Those two are also even numbers. Let's divide by 2, one more time. Now the answer is:

$$1\frac{1}{13}$$

When you add 4 cards to 1 full deck, you have $1\frac{1}{13}$ decks of cards. The number above, $1\frac{1}{13}$, is called a *mixed number*. Whenever you have a whole number next to a fraction, it is called a mixed number.

Let's try one more. This time we will start with a *mixed number* and then we will turn it into an improper fraction.

Let's say we have $4\frac{1}{2}$ dozen eggs. There are 12 eggs in 1 dozen. I will write 1 dozen eggs as a fraction.

$$\frac{12}{12}$$

Now I will write 2 dozen eggs as an improper fraction.

$$\frac{24}{12}$$

Add 12 more eggs to the numerator to show 3 dozen eggs as an improper fraction.

$$\frac{36}{12}$$

Can you guess how to write 4 dozen eggs as an improper fraction?

$$\frac{48}{12}$$

We are trying to write $4\frac{1}{2}$ dozen eggs as an improper fraction, so we need to add half a dozen more to the 48/12. Half a dozen eggs could be written as 6/12, so let's add them up.

$$\frac{48}{12} + \frac{6}{12} = \frac{54}{12}$$

Remember, just add the numerators. You can't change how many eggs are in 1 dozen, so the denominator has to stay 12.

Let's try a more difficult problem. This time, we'll start with an improper fraction and then we'll turn it into a mixed number.

$$\frac{412}{15}$$

Look at the fraction above. This fraction is saying that we have 412 pieces of something, but it only takes 15 of those pieces to make 1. We want to turn $\frac{412}{15}$ into a whole number and a fraction, you know, a mixed number.

So how do we write that as a mixed number? Well, that is a division problem. How many times does 15 go into 412?

```
          27 R 7
     15) 412
          30
         112
         105
           7
```

The answer is 27 times with a remainder of 7, so $\frac{412}{15}$ equals $27\frac{7}{15}$. Do you see how we put the remainder over the denominator? Those are the left over pieces.

In fact, in higher math you will learn that the "line" or "slash" in a fraction is actually a symbol for division! Look at that last example again.

$$\frac{412}{15}$$

This fraction is read "four hundred twelve fifteenths." But it is also correct to read this as "four hundred twelve *divided by* fifteen." Let's prove this theory with a fraction you already know.

You know that $\frac{1}{4}$ of a dollar is 25 cents. Now read $\frac{1}{4}$ as "one divided by four." Let's do the math.

$$4\overline{)1.00}^{.25}$$

See, 1/4 does equal .25 and 1 divided by 4 is also .25.

Earlier we learned that $\frac{5}{4}$ = $1.25. Let's prove it by reading the fraction as 5 *divided by* 4. I'll do the math.

$$4\overline{)5.00}^{1.25}$$

Sure enough, $\frac{5}{4}$ does equal 1.25.

Sometimes it is hard to remember if it is the numerator or the denominator that goes on the outside of the division bar. Here is a way to make sure you are dividing correctly.

Always start with a problem whose answer you already know. You know that 1/2 is the same as 50 cents or .50, so let's look at the math for 1 divided by 2.

$$2\overline{)1.0}^{.5}$$

When you put the 2 on the outside of the division bar, you will get the correct answer .5.

But if you divide incorrectly because you can't remember if it's the numerator or the denominator that goes on the outside, then this is the answer you'll get...

$$1\overline{)2.0}^{2.0}$$

TWO? Well, we know that 1/2 is not 2; this is not the correct order. So when you are trying to recall which number goes where, think back on how to divide 1/2 to get .5. Then put your numerator in the same place we put our 1; inside the division bar.

If you're using a calculator, just read the fraction as you type. For example, 1/5 is read as "one divided by five," so type in 1...divide...5, to turn a fraction into a decimal number with a calculator.

One more time, just to make sure you fully understand improper fractions and mixed numbers. Let's turn this next improper fraction into a mixed number.

$$\frac{22}{7}$$

This is a division problem, so divide.

$$22 \div 7 = 3 \; with \; a \; remainder \; of \; 1$$

Put the remainder over the denominator to create a fraction.

$$\frac{22}{7} = 3\frac{1}{7}$$

Now we will do the opposite operation. We will turn a mixed number into an improper fraction. Below is a mixed number. Let's convert it into an improper fraction.

$$5\frac{3}{4}$$

Start by multiplying these two numbers. The whole number times the denominator, 5 x 4 = 20. Next, add the numerator to that answer, 20 + 3.

$$5\frac{3}{4}$$

Put that answer over the denominator.

$$\frac{23}{4}$$

And TADA you have an improper fraction. Look at that improper fraction as a division problem and do the math.

$$\begin{array}{r} 5\ R3 \\ 4\overline{)\ 23} \\ \underline{20} \\ 3 \end{array}$$

Put the remainder over the denominator, and you are back to $5\frac{3}{4}$...tada!

Here are the mathematical steps to turn each mixed number into an improper fraction:

- First multiply the whole number by the denominator.
- Add the numerator to your answer.
- Put that total over the denominator.

Use those steps to help you complete the next worksheet. If you are confused, or if you get more than 2 wrong on the worksheet, read this lesson again.

If you are having difficulties remembering all the steps, then go to our website, Learnmathfastbooks.com, and print off the Fraction Blaster. That two sided sheet lists all the steps necessary to add, subtract, multiply, and divide fractions. You can use it while you complete the worksheets.

If you know how to read music, then watch our video called A Math Lesson for Musicians.

The next time you sit down to eat a meal, look for one big item on your plate that can be sliced up, for example, a pancake, a sandwich, or an apple. Slice it up evenly and count up the number of pieces; that's your denominator. Now as you eat each fraction of your sandwich, or whatever, subtract that amount and figure out how much you have left.

WORKSHEET 2-10

Convert each mixed number into an improper fraction.

1.	$4\frac{5}{8}$	2.	$2\frac{3}{4}$

3.	$1\frac{7}{10}$	4.	$6\frac{8}{20}$

5.	$8\frac{1}{3}$	6.	$5\frac{6}{9}$

7.	$3\frac{2}{11}$	8.	$7\frac{1}{5}$

Convert each improper fraction into a mixed or whole number.

9.	$\frac{10}{8}$	10.	$\frac{21}{10}$

11.	$\frac{22}{7}$	12.	$\frac{26}{5}$

13.	$\frac{400}{12}$	14.	$\frac{386}{3}$

15.	$\frac{200}{10}$	16.	$\frac{3}{1}$

Now that you know how to convert mixed numbers into improper fractions, let's learn how to add them together.

Below are two mixed numbers. We will add them together.

$$2\frac{2}{8} + 4\frac{5}{8} =$$

Start by adding the whole numbers together, 2 + 4 = 6. Then add the fractions together.

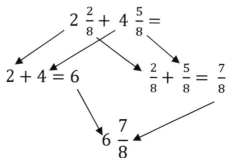

That's all there is to it! Add the whole numbers together; then add the fractions together.

When you add these next two mixed numbers together, the fraction in the answer will be improper. Can you guess what to do next?

$$5\frac{7}{10} + 3\frac{7}{10} = 8\frac{14}{10}$$

Earlier we learned how to turn an improper fraction into a mixed number. That's what we need to do with this improper fraction.

$$\frac{14}{10} = 1\frac{4}{10}$$

Now add that mixed number to the whole number 8 and we have the answer.

$$8 + 1\,\frac{4}{10} = 9\,\frac{4}{10}$$

Looking at $\frac{4}{10}$, you can see that both those numbers are even, so you know we can reduce that fraction by dividing both the numerator and the denominator by 2.

$$9\,\frac{4}{10} = 9\,\frac{2}{5}$$

Let's try a more difficult one. This time you will need to find a common denominator before you can add.

$$5\,\frac{2}{3} + 6\,\frac{7}{9} =$$

First, add the whole numbers.

$$5 + 6 = 11$$

Next, find a common denominator, so you can add the fractions together.

$$\frac{2}{3}\ becomes\ \frac{6}{9}$$

Add the fractions together.

$$\frac{6}{9} + \frac{7}{9} = \frac{13}{9}$$

Convert the improper fraction into a mixed number. Divide, $13 \div 9 = 1\,R4$. Put the remainder over the denominator, $1\,\frac{4}{9}$. Add that to the whole number from above.

$$11 + 1\,\frac{4}{9} = 12\,\frac{4}{9}$$

Try adding mixed numbers on your own. Complete the next worksheet.

Name: _____   Date: _____

WORKSHEET 2-11

Add the following mixed numbers.

1. $5\frac{2}{8} + 4\frac{3}{8} =$

2. $2\frac{6}{12} + 6\frac{5}{12} =$

3. $3\frac{3}{16} + 3\frac{2}{16} =$

4. $5\frac{4}{10} + 3\frac{1}{5} =$

5. $4\frac{7}{8} + 3\frac{1}{16} =$

6. $18\frac{2}{5} + 3\frac{5}{25} =$

7. $7\frac{8}{32} + 5\frac{7}{8} =$

8. $11\frac{8}{48} + 9\frac{21}{24} =$

9.   Jennifer poured $1\frac{1}{2}$ cups of sand into a bucket. Jessi added $\frac{3}{4}$ cups of sand to the bucket. How much sand is in the bucket now?

10.   There are two books stacked up on the table. One book measures $1\frac{7}{8}$ inches. The other book is $1\frac{5}{16}$ inches tall. How tall is the stack of two books?

11.   Pat kicked the ball $36\frac{1}{3}$ feet. Lynda kicked the ball $4\frac{3}{4}$ feet farther. How far did Linda kick the ball?

12.   Maggi worked three days last week. On Monday, she worked $5\frac{1}{2}$ hours. On Wednesday, she worked $6\frac{3}{4}$ hours. On Friday, she worked $7\frac{1}{4}$ hours. How many hours did she work last week?

13.   When Debbie got her puppy, he was $7\frac{5}{8}$ inches tall. Since then he has grown $2\frac{3}{4}$ inches more. How tall is the puppy now?

Subtracting mixed numbers works the same way as addition. Subtract the whole number and then subtract the fractions. Look at the problem below. First, I subtracted the whole numbers, 4 – 3 = 1. Next, I subtracted the fractions. Since this fraction is bigger than this fraction, the math is easy.

$$4\frac{5}{8} - 3\frac{2}{8} = 1\frac{3}{8}$$

The math is 5 – 2 = 3. That problem was nice and simple. But sometimes, you will run into a problem like the one below. When you try to subtract these fractions, you end up with 1 – 3. Uh-oh.

$$5\frac{1}{4} - 4\frac{3}{4} =$$

When this happens you can to turn both mixed numbers into improper fractions and then subtract.

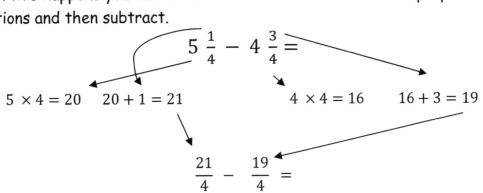

Now you can subtract the numerators, 21 – 19 = 2. That answer can be reduced.

$$\frac{21}{4} - \frac{19}{4} = \frac{2}{4} = \frac{1}{2}$$

Here is a really difficult one. It has a little bit of everything involved. You will need to get common denominators, you will have to turn the mixed numbers into improper fractions, and then you will need to turn that answer back into a mixed number. But if you are this far into this book, I know you can do it. You may want to get a calculator.

$$7\frac{3}{8} - 5\frac{4}{7} =$$

Let's start by getting a common denominator. Can you think of a number that is divisible by both 8 and 7? That's a tough one. Let's just multiply them together, to get 56 for a common denominator. And remember, whatever you do to the denominator, you MUST do to the numerator.

$$7\frac{3}{8} - 5\frac{4}{7} = \qquad 7\frac{21}{56} - 5\frac{32}{56} =$$

OK...we still can't subtract, so let's convert these mixed numbers into improper fractions.

$$7\frac{21}{56} - 5\frac{32}{56} = \quad \frac{}{56} - \frac{}{56} =$$

$7 \times 56 = 392 \qquad 392 + 21 = 413$

$5 \times 56 = 280 \qquad 280 + 32 = 312$

$$\frac{413}{56} - \frac{312}{56} = \frac{101}{56}$$

Now we can subtract! But we still have to convert this improper fraction into a mixed number. Divide, $101 \div 56 = 1 \ with \ Remainder \ 45.$

$$7\frac{3}{8} - 5\frac{4}{7} = 1\frac{45}{56}$$

That is the final answer. If you followed along with that last example and you understood all of it, complete the next worksheet.

Name: _____   Date: _____

WORKSHEET 2-12

Subtract the following mixed numbers.

1. $7\frac{3}{8} - 5\frac{1}{8} =$

2. $9\frac{2}{3} - 3\frac{1}{3} =$

3. $20\frac{5}{7} - 15\frac{1}{3} =$

4. $14\frac{1}{2} - 6\frac{1}{8} =$

5. $11\frac{9}{16} - 6\frac{1}{2} =$

6. $14\frac{3}{4} - 8\frac{7}{24} =$

7. $9\frac{2}{3} - 3\frac{1}{3} =$

8. $15\frac{1}{4} - 9\frac{5}{8} =$

9. Yesterday there was $4\frac{1}{8}$ inches of rain in the rain gauge. Today it measures $5\frac{3}{16}$ inches of rain. How much did it rain in the last day?

10. Last year our apple tree was $8\frac{1}{4}$ feet tall. This year the apple tree is $10\frac{1}{2}$ feet tall. How much did the tree grow during the last year?

11. Linda kicked the ball $44\frac{5}{12}$ feet. Pat kicked the ball $41\frac{1}{12}$ feet. How much farther did Linda kick the ball than Pat?

12. Teresa added $1\frac{1}{3}$ cups of water to the fish bowl. Now the fish bowl has a total of $22\frac{1}{2}$ cups of water. How much water was in the bowl before Teresa added water?

13. The first song on the CD was $3\frac{1}{4}$ minutes long. The entire CD was 45 minutes long. How long were the remaining songs?

LESSON 13: MULTIPLYING MIXED NUMBERS

Next, we will learn how to multiply mixed numbers. It's not quite the same as addition and subtraction, but close. With multiplication you MUST convert each mixed number into an improper fraction before you can multiply. Take a look at the example below.

$$3\frac{1}{2} \times 4\frac{3}{8} =$$

We can't just multiply 3 x 4 and then multiply the fractions. That would give us the wrong answer. We MUST make them both improper fractions. Here is the math I used to make them both improper.

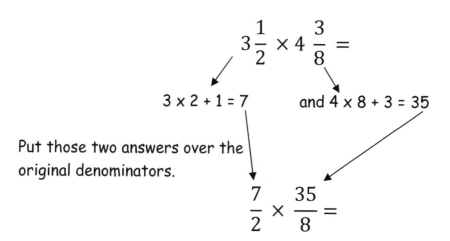

$$3\frac{1}{2} \times 4\frac{3}{8} =$$

3 x 2 + 1 = 7   and 4 x 8 + 3 = 35

Put those two answers over the original denominators.

$$\frac{7}{2} \times \frac{35}{8} =$$

Don't bother getting a common denominator; that's for addition and subtraction. Instead, just multiply straight across.

$$\frac{7}{2} \times \frac{35}{8} = \frac{245}{16}$$

Turn $\frac{245}{16}$ back into a mixed number. Divide, 245 ÷ 16 = 15 $\frac{5}{16}$.

Remember, before you can multiply mixed numbers, you MUST turn them into improper fractions first. Complete the next worksheet.

WORKSHEET 2-13

Multiply the following mixed numbers.

1. $3\frac{4}{7} \times 2\frac{3}{10} =$

2. $2\frac{9}{10} \times 4\frac{3}{8} =$

3. $4\frac{1}{3} \times 3\frac{7}{8} =$

4. $10\frac{1}{2} \times 3\frac{1}{3} =$

5. $8 \times 3\frac{6}{10} =$ Hint: $8 = \frac{8}{1}$

To find one half of any number, multiply it by $\frac{1}{2}$.

6. How long is $\frac{1}{2}$ of $4\frac{5}{8}$ miles?

7. How much is $\frac{1}{2}$ of $\frac{1}{2}$?

8. How much is $\frac{1}{2}$ of $3\frac{7}{8}$?

9. I taped 3 small pieces of paper together to make one long piece of paper. Each piece of paper was $5\frac{3}{4}$ inches long. How long is the paper now that the 3 pieces are taped together?

10. Sherry wants to put 3 photographs onto 1 page of her scrapbook. Each picture is $2\frac{1}{8}$ inches long. The page is 7 inches long. Will all 3 pictures fit on 1 page?

Dividing mixed numbers is pretty much the same as multiplying mixed numbers. Start by converting the mixed numbers into improper fractions. Then, flip the second improper fraction to get the reciprocal, BEFORE you multiply straight across.

$1\frac{1}{2} \div 3\frac{1}{3} =$ First, convert the mixed numbers into improper fractions.

$\frac{3}{2} \div \frac{10}{3} =$ Next, flip the second fraction to get the reciprocal.

$\frac{3}{2} \times \frac{3}{10} =$ Multiply straight across.

$\frac{3}{2} \times \frac{3}{10} = \frac{9}{20}$

It couldn't be any simpler. Just follow the three steps: convert, flip, multiply. Don't bother getting a common denominator – that's for adding and subtracting.

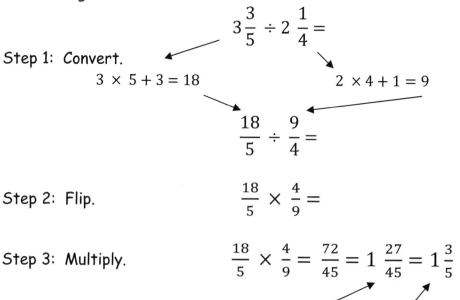

Step 1: Convert.
$3 \times 5 + 3 = 18$ $2 \times 4 + 1 = 9$

Step 2: Flip.

Step 3: Multiply.

Convert back into a mixed number and reduce.

WORKSHEET 2-14

1. $2\frac{1}{11} \div 4\frac{5}{8} =$

2. $4\frac{4}{9} \div 1\frac{3}{5} =$

3. $2\frac{1}{12} \div 3\frac{2}{7} =$

4. $3\frac{3}{8} \div 5\frac{2}{9} =$

5. $44 \div \frac{3}{11} =$

To find half of any number, you can divide by 2, or $\frac{2}{1}$.

6. Brianna wants to hang a picture in the center of the wall. The wall measures $8\frac{1}{4}$ feet wide. To find the center of the wall, she needs to find the half way point. What is half of $8\frac{1}{4}$ feet?

7. Tia is making some cookies. The recipe will make 48 cookies. Tia only wants to make 24 cookies, so she is only using half the amount of each ingredient. The recipe calls for $2\frac{1}{4}$ cups of flour. How much flour should Tia use?

8. Austin wants to make as many plaster molds as he can. Each mold needs $\frac{1}{4}$ cup of plaster. He has $3\frac{3}{4}$ cups of plaster. How many molds can he make?

The next mathematical skill you need to learn is called cross canceling. You will find this is a very handy tool to have in your math tool box. Look at the math problem below.

$$\frac{8}{24} \times \frac{3}{8} =$$

You know how to solve this problem; you just multiply straight across. If you multiply 8 x 3 and then 24 x 8, you will get an answer of $\frac{24}{192}$. Then you reduce and eventually you'll get down to $\frac{1}{8}$. Now let's look at cross canceling. Here is the same problem.

$$\frac{8}{24} \times \frac{3}{8} =$$

Do you see how those two 8's are diagonal from each other? When you have two of the same numbers diagonal from each other like that, you can cancel them out and turn them both into a 1, like this:

$$\frac{\overset{1}{\cancel{8}}}{24} \times \frac{3}{\underset{1}{\cancel{8}}} =$$ Now the new problem is $\frac{1}{24} \times \frac{3}{1} =$

But wait! Look at the other two numbers that are diagonal from each other, 24 and 3. These two numbers are both divisible by 3, so we can reduce these numbers too. 3 ÷ 3 = 1 and 24 ÷ 3 = 8.

$$\frac{1}{\underset{8}{\cancel{24}}} \times \frac{\overset{1}{\cancel{3}}}{1} =$$ Now the new problem is $\frac{1}{8} \times \frac{1}{1}$. Now do the math.

$1 \times 1 = 1$ and $8 \times 1 = 8$, so the answer is $\dfrac{1}{8}$. Do you see how cross canceling can be your best friend when it comes to multiplying fractions? Let's try cross cancelling with a division problem this time.

$\dfrac{4}{16} \div \dfrac{2}{8} =$ You **MUST** get the reciprocal first and then cross cancel because cross canceling is ONLY for multiplication.

$\dfrac{4}{16} \times \dfrac{8}{2} =$ Now we are ready to cross cancel because we are multiplying.

$\dfrac{\overset{2}{\cancel{4}}}{16} \times \dfrac{8}{\underset{1}{\cancel{2}}} =$ 4 and 2 are both divisible by 2, so divide both by 2.

$\dfrac{2}{\underset{2}{\cancel{16}}} \times \dfrac{\overset{1}{\cancel{8}}}{1} =$ 8 and 16 are both divisible by 8, so divide both by 8.

$\dfrac{2}{2} \times \dfrac{1}{1} =$ Here is our new problem. Now we can multiply.

$\dfrac{2}{2} \times \dfrac{1}{1} = \dfrac{2}{2} = 1$

But remember, cross cancelling is for multiplying fractions. The only reason you can use this skill when dividing is because once you get the reciprocal, the math turns into a multiplication problem; that's when we use cross cancelling.

Cross cancelling makes multiplying fractions easier! Try some on your own on the next worksheet.

WORKSHEET 2-15

Multiply and divide the following fractions. Cross cancel whenever possible. When dividing, remember to flip before you cancel.

1. $\dfrac{8}{16} \times \dfrac{8}{10} =$

2. $\dfrac{3}{48} \times \dfrac{6}{21} =$

3. $\dfrac{7}{12} \times \dfrac{6}{10} =$

4. $\dfrac{2}{10} \times \dfrac{5}{24} =$

5. $\dfrac{8}{56} \div \dfrac{4}{7} =$

6. $\dfrac{9}{64} \div \dfrac{3}{8} =$

7. $\dfrac{5}{42} \div \dfrac{2}{6} =$

8. $\dfrac{7}{35} \div \dfrac{1}{7} =$

9. $\dfrac{3}{24} \div \dfrac{3}{6} =$

10. $\dfrac{9}{27} \div \dfrac{3}{9} =$

CHAPTER 1 REVIEW TEST

Solve the following problems. Reduce all answers down to the smallest denominator. Convert all improper fractions into mixed numbers.

1. $\frac{1}{8} + 2\frac{3}{8} =$

2. $3\frac{4}{6} + \frac{1}{5} =$

3. $\frac{5}{8} - \frac{1}{16} =$

4. $5\frac{5}{12} - 2\frac{3}{4} =$

5. $2\frac{5}{8} \times 3 =$

6. $3\frac{4}{8} \div 4 =$

7.   I have a stack of baseball cards that measures $\frac{1}{2}$ inch high. Your stack of baseball cards is $\frac{1}{8}$ inch taller than mine. How tall is your stack of cards?

8.   Brendon cut a sandwich into 8 pieces. John ate one of the pieces. How much of a sandwich does he have left?

9.   There is a recipe for 4 dozen cookies on the next page. We want to make only 2 dozen, so we need to cut the recipe in half. Rewrite the amounts needed to make half the recipe.

$2\frac{1}{4}$ Cups of flour

$\frac{3}{4}$ Cup sugar

$\frac{1}{2}$ Cup brown sugar

$\frac{2}{3}$ Cup butter

2   Eggs

1   Teaspoon baking soda

$\frac{1}{3}$ Tablepoon salt

$\frac{1}{4}$ Teaspoon vanilla

10.   A newspaper costs 8/10 of a dollar. How much does it cost?

11.   Kathy wants to hang a picture in the center of a wall. The wall measures 37 3/4" wide. She needs to find the center of the wall. Half of 37 3/4" would be the center. How far from the edge of the wall should Kathy measure, to make sure the nail is in the center of the wall?

12.   Write a fraction to show what line the arrow is pointing to.

CHAPTER 2

PERCENTAGES

Can you solve these problems?

What is 20% of $55.00?
What is 30% of 5000?
A dime is what percentage of a dollar?

If these questions are challenging for you, please read on. You will be able to answer these questions easily in about an hour.

LESSON 16: DECIMAL NUMBERS, PERCENTAGES, AND FRACTIONS

Let's start off with something you already know. Here is one dollar.

Here is what you already know about one whole dollar.

- $\frac{1}{2}$ of 1 dollar is 50 cents
- 50 cents is written as $0.50

But did you know that $\frac{1}{2}$ is how you write a fraction to equal 50 cents? And did you know .50 is the decimal number for $\frac{1}{2}$? They mean the same thing.

If you want to know how much is half of any number, multiply that number by $\frac{1}{2}$ or by .50; they mean the same thing.

Let me prove it. You know that half of 10 is 5, right? Here's the math using fractions.

$$\frac{10}{1} \times \frac{1}{2} = \frac{10}{2} \; reduces \; to \; 5$$

Remember, the number 10, written as a fraction is 10/1 because the denominator tells us it takes 1 piece to make 1 and we have 10 of those pieces.

I can also prove 5 is half of 10 by using a decimal number, instead of a fraction. I will use .5 because that is the same thing as $\frac{1}{2}$.

$$10 \times .5 = 5.0$$

Do you see how $\frac{1}{2}$ and .5 are the same? One is a fraction and one is a decimal number. It is also true to say:

$$\frac{1}{2} = .5000000000000$$
$$\tfrac{1}{2} = 0000.5000$$

Don't let all those zeros confuse you. The numbers above are the same. The zeros before and after .5 don't change the number; it is still half.

The same is true if you have $1.00. You also have $1.0000000000000 and you have $ 000001.00. All those numbers equal 1 dollar because the decimal point didn't move.

Now don't confuse a decimal point with a comma. A comma is completely different. A large number can have more than one comma, but there can only be one decimal point in any number. For example, one million is written 1,000,000. That is not the same as 1 dollar written with extra zeros:

$$1.000000$$

It is important to read the decimal point and commas as much as it is to read the numbers themselves.

When we are talking about money, the decimal point is there to tell us that all the numbers to the right are pennies, dimes, and nickels - you know, less than one dollar.

Remember, 1 is a whole number. It is 1 whole *anything*, but here we are talking about 1 whole dollar. If there are any numbers after the decimal point, then we have some cents.

Let's get back to the earlier statement of...

$$\frac{1}{2} = .50$$

We know this is true, so let's see how to change these numbers into percentages. The symbol for percentage is %.

If you split something "fifty-fifty" with your friend, you know that they get half and so do you because "fifty-fifty" means 50% for you and 50% for your friend.

If an $800 couch is marked down 50%, we know that means it is half price. The couch now costs $400.

In order to find out how much is 50% of 800, we need to multiply. You already know the answer, but we need to learn how to figure it out mathematically, since it won't always be so simple.

We will need to turn 50% into a number we can work with mathematically.

Math teachers tell you to *move the decimal point over two spaces to the left when converting percentages into decimal numbers*, which is true, but that is one more rule you have to remember. Instead, let's think about it logically. How long is a **cent**ury? It is 100 years. Do you know how many **cent**imeters are in a meter? There are 100. How many **cent**s are in a dollar? Again it is 100. The root word *cent* means 100.

When we say "per-**cent**" it means "per 100." Let's say we have a big jar full of jelly beans. I tell you that 50% of the jelly beans are red. That means that for every 100 jelly beans, 50 of them will be red. It's *50 per 100*.

To multiply a number by 50%, we have to change it, so it looks like money. 50% (50 per-cent) turns into $0.50 (50 cents). Drop the $ sign and the extra zeros. Now that's a number we can multiply with: .5 (point 5).

75% is written .75, and 10% is written .10; however, 9% is NOT .9. That's how you write 90%. To write 9% as a decimal number, write .09. There has to be a zero in the tenths column because there are 0 dimes.

Can you guess how to write 38% as a decimal number? It's just like thirty eight cents, so the answer is .38. If you wanted to know 38% of a number, you would multiply it by .38. Now let's do the math, to find out what 50% of 800 equals.

800 x 50%   or in other words   800 x .50

$$
\begin{array}{r}
800 \\
\times\ .50 \\
\hline
000 \\
40000\ \\
\hline
400.00
\end{array}
$$

Since we multiplied by .50, we need to move the decimal point in the answer over, to the left, the same amount of numbers. In this case the decimal point in .50 has been moved over 2 numbers from the end. So move the decimal point in the answer over 2 numbers from the end too. That will turn 40000 into 400.00, which proves that 50% of 800 is indeed 400.

Just to make sure you are clear on exactly what 50% means, I'll give you some examples.

Point five (.5) or fifty cents ($0.50) is half of one dollar, but 50% is half of anything. For example you could say, "In a room full of 30 people, 50% were girls." You wouldn't say .5 were girls because that would mean there was half a person and she was a girl. We use the term 50% to represent half, when we are referring to more than one.

Here are a few more examples of when it is appropriate to use ½, $0.50, or 50%.

- I want pepperoni on 1/2 of the pizza.
- We need two quarters for the claw machine. That's $0.50.
- You showed up late for work 2 times in the last 4 days; that means you were late 50% of the time.

Let's further explore the relationship between fractions, decimal point numbers, and percentages. 50% of a dollar is 50 cents; however, 50% of the houses in your neighborhood could be 24. There is no set number to represent 50%, it is just half of anything.

50% of a deck of cards is 26 cards.
50% off a book that costs $24 is $12.
50% of the number of months in a year is 6.

Let's prove each of those statements with math. First, the deck of cards; a full deck is 52 cards. 50% is written as .50 so...

$$
\begin{array}{r}
52 \\
\times\ .50 \\
\hline
00 \\
2600 \\
\hline
2600
\end{array}
$$

Don't forget to move the decimal point over the same amount of spaces as .50. Now 2600 becomes 26, so it is true to say that 50% of a deck of cards is 26 cards.

Just for fun, let's do the same math with more zeros.

```
          52
      × .500000
          00
         000
        0000
       00000
      000000
     26000000
     26000000
```

.500000 has the decimal point 6 numbers from the end, so we need to do the same with the answer, 26000000. Moving the decimal point over 6 numbers turns 26000000 into 26.000000, which is 26.

Now we'll try the same problem with less zeros.

```
      52
    × .5
     260
```

Move the decimal point over 1 place, since we multiplied by .5. That turns 260 into 26.0. So you see, all those zeros won't change the answer.

Now we will prove that if you take 50% off the price of a book that cost $24, your discount is $12. Here is the math.

```
      24
    × .50
      00
     1200
     1200
```

Move the decimal point over 2 numbers and we get $12.

And finally, let's prove that 50% of a year is 6 months. This time we will multiply by .5, since it is the same thing as .50 or 50%.

A full year is 12 months, so let's do the math.

$$
\begin{array}{r}
12 \\
\times\ .5 \\
\hline
60
\end{array}
$$

Move the decimal point over one space and we end up with 6. ½ of 12 months is 6. Here is the same math with fractions.

$$\frac{1}{2} \times \frac{12}{1} = \frac{12}{2}$$

Anytime you want a whole number as a fraction, just put the number over a 1. Next, multiply straight across and you get 12/2, which reduces down to 6. That proves that half of 12 is 6.

Now that you completely understand what "half" is, let's bump it up to ¾... or 75 cents...or 75%.

Let's go back to one dollar in change; quarters this time.

- 3 of the 4 quarters are ¾ of the whole dollar
- 3 quarters equal 75 cents
- 75% of the dollar is 75 cents
- .75 means 7 dimes and 5 pennies

75 cents is 7 dimes and 5 pennies. The 5 is in the "hundredths" column. 5 pennies is written as 5/100. Going back to our fractions lesson, we can write the addition of 7 dimes and 5 pennies like this:

$$\frac{7}{10} + \frac{5}{100} =$$

Find a common denominator; 100 works. That will turn 7/10 into 70/100, so our new problem looks like this:

$$\frac{70}{100} + \frac{5}{100} = \frac{75}{100} \; reduces\; to\; \frac{3}{4}$$

> Just like the 3 coins on the last page; 3 quarters.

Let's take a closer look at 5/100. That equals 5 pennies. 5 cents is written as .05. Can you guess how to write $\frac{5}{100}$ as a percentage? It would be 5%.

Below is a table. One column has a fraction, one column has a percentage, and one column has a number with a decimal point. Each number is the same portion of a dollar. Look at the table below.

Fraction	Decimal pt.	Percentage
1/4	.25	25%

Think about a dollar. ¼ of 1 dollar is 25 cents. And 25 cents is 25% of a dollar, so all 3 numbers above represent the same amount of a dollar.

This time you fill in the blank box.

Fraction	Decimal pt.	Percentage
	.50	50%

50 percent of a dollar is the same as 50 cents. How much of a dollar is 50 cents? It is half of the dollar. There are a lot of different ways to write ½ as a fraction. You could start with 50/100, chop 1 zero off the numerator and 1 zero off the denominator, to get down to 5/10. Divide both by 5, to get down to 1/2.

If you understand everything so far, complete the next worksheet. If you are a little frustrated because you don't get it yet, go back and read this chapter again. It will make more sense the second time.

WORKSHEET 2-16

1.   Fill in the blank boxes below.

Fraction	Decimal pt.	Percentage
$\frac{1}{2}$		50%
8/10	.80	
	.32	32%
1/100		1%
2/10	.2	
		99%
7/100		
	.33	
		10%

2.   How much is 10% of a dollar?

3.   Write 56 cents as a fraction. Reduce your answer.

4.   Write $\frac{1}{2}$ as a decimal number.

5.   There are 342 jelly beans in a jar. 50% of them are blue. How many blue jelly beans are in the jar?

6.   How many years are in a **cent**ury?

7.   How many **cents** are in a dollar?

8.   What does the word per**cent** mean?

9.   There were 100 people in the room.   99 of them were under the age of 70. What percentage of the people in the room were over age 70?

Can you guess how much money you would have, if you had 150/100 of a dollar?

When the numerator is bigger than the denominator, it means more than one. Looking at the fraction above, if you had 150 pennies, how much money would you have? $1.50

Therefore, 150/100 = 1.5 or $1.50 or 150%

A businessman may say, "Sales are up 150% this month." What does that mean?

Let's say a fast food restaurant sells 800 cheeseburgers in July. If they sell 800 cheeseburgers in August, sales are the same. There is a 0% change in sales.

In order to increase sales by 50%, they would need to sell 50% of 800 MORE cheeseburgers. 50% of 800 is 400, so they would need to sell 1200 cheeseburgers just to have a 50% increase in sales.

So how many cheeseburgers do they have to sell to have a 100% increase in sales? 100% of 800 is 800, so they would need to sell 1600 cheeseburgers.

To have a 150% increase in sales, they would need to sell 1200 more cheeseburgers than the month before; for a total of 2000 cheeseburgers. Let's do the math.

$$800 \times 150\% =$$

How would you write 150% as a decimal number? Think about money. 150 "per-cent" is the same as 150 "cents." We write that as 1.50, but let's drop the extra zero to keep it simple.

$$800 \times 1.5 = 1200$$

They would need to sell 1200 cheeseburgers in addition to the 800 cheeseburgers they sold the month before, to have an increase of 150% in sales.

Let's make sure you completely understand the relationship between fractions, percentages, and decimal point numbers inside and out.

- ½ of a dollar is 50 cents, written as .50
- 50% of a dollar is 50 cents
- 1/2 means 1 divided by 2

When you want to know half of a number, multiply it by .5 or $\frac{1}{2}$. The answer will equal half of that number. Let's try a few, use a calculator if you'd like.

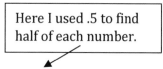

Here I used .5 to find half of each number.

I multiplied the same numbers by $\frac{1}{2}$ on this side.

12 x .5 = 6.0 Yep, that's true, 6 *is* half of 12. $\frac{12}{1} \times \frac{1}{2} = \frac{12}{2} = 6$

32 x .5 = 16.0 also true, 16 is 50% of 32. $\frac{32}{1} \times \frac{1}{2} = \frac{32}{2} = 16$

8 x .5 = 4.0 again true, ½ of 8 is 4. $\frac{8}{1} \times \frac{1}{2} = \frac{8}{2} = 4$

Do you see how any number times 50% is half of that number?

Now let's examine 25%.

- 25% of a dollar is one quarter
- One quarter is written as ¼
- ¼ means one of four pieces
- 1 divided by 4 is .25
- .25 is twenty-five cents
- Twenty-five cents is 25% of one dollar

Now the next time you see something marked down 25%, you should be able to figure out the discount in your head because 25% of something is ¼ of it.

To figure out how much ¼ of something is, we could divide it by 4. Does that make sense? Remember our sandwich from the fractions chapter? ¼ of the sandwich was 1 of the 4 pieces. Therefore, 25% of something is the same as 1/4 of it.

Let's say you see a shirt for $12 and it is marked down 25%. 25% is the same thing as ¼. One fourth of 12 is the same thing as 12 divided by 4.

$$12 \div 4 = 3$$

So, 25% of 12 is 3; that's the amount of the discount. Just subtract 3 from 12 and you have the new price for the shirt...$9.

Try one on your own. See if you can figure out the new price in your head.

A TV is advertised for $400. Today it is 25% off. What is the price of the TV today?

In your head, figure out how much is 25% of 400. Remember 25% is the same as ¼.

¼ of 400 is...100, so that's how much the discount is. Now subtract 100 from 400 and you have the new price of the TV...$300.

Now we will look at 10% of 300, 10% of 50, and 10% of 1061. See if you can see a pattern here (Remember 10% is written as .10, just like 10 cents).

300	50	1061
× .10	× .10	× .10
30.00	5.00	106.10

Look at that! Every time you multiply a number by 10%, the answer is the same number with the decimal point moved over one space, to the left.

That's because 10% is the same as 10 cents. And .10 is the same as .1. So every time you multiply a number by 10%, it is the same thing as multiplying by 1 and moving the decimal point over one space.

Therefore, 10% of 800 must be 80 and 10% of 3245 is 324.5. Can you guess how much is 10% of 10780? Just move the decimal point over one space. But you may ask, "Where is the decimal point in 10780?" If you don't see a decimal point, it is assumed to be a whole number. Therefore, the decimal point is at the end, so move it over one space to the left and you have your answer. 10% of 10780 is 1078.0 or drop the zero on the end and it is 1078.

If that makes sense to you, complete the next worksheet. If you are confused, remember that 50% of anything is half of it, so divide by 2. 25% of anything is one fourth of it, so divide by 4. And to find 10% of a number, just move the decimal number one space to the left.

WORKSHEET 2-17

How much is 10% of:

1. 100
2. 80
3. 75
4. 850
5. 962

How much is 25% of:

6. 100
7. 12
8. 40
9. 200
10. 16

11. Write .25 as a fraction. Reduce your answer.
12. Write .50 as a fraction. Reduce your answer.
13. Write one tenth as a percentage.
14. How much is 10% of 2,457?
15. How much is 10% of one million?

16. How much is 10% of a dollar?
17. Judy bought a case of ice tea. There are 10 bottles of tea in each case. She put 20% of them in the refrigerator. How many bottles did Judy put in the refrigerator?
18. Daryl went fishing. He caught 40 fish. 50% of the fish weighed over 10 pounds. How many fish weighed less than 10 pounds?
19. Marion took her dog out for a 2 hour walk. Marion's dog was on the leash 50% of the time. How long was her dog on a leash?
20. Chuck is 70 years old. He has lived in Seattle 50% of his life. How long has he lived in Seattle?

LESSON 18: 20%, 30%, AND 40% OF A NUMBER

I have an easy trick to figuring out 20% of a number. Just figure out how much is 10%, since it's easy to figure out in your head, then just double that number. For example:

10% of 600 is 60.

To figure out 20% of 600, just double the answer for 10%; 60 + 60 = 120. Therefore, 20% of 600 is 120.

If you had a calculator, you would type 600 x .20, but who needs a calculator when you can quickly figure 10% + 10% in your head. Here's another example:

What is 20% of 250?

I can quickly figure out 10% of 250 and then double that number. I can quickly see that 10% of 250 is 25 and to double that number in my head is...50.

You can do the same for 30% or 40% of a number. Just figure out 10% and then multiply it by 3 or 4. For example:

What is 30% of 50?

Immediately I can tell that 10% of 50 is 5, so let's triple that to get 30% or just multiply it by 3.

5 x 3 = 15 therefore,
30% of 50 = 15

Does that make sense? Basically, we are adding 10% + 10% + 10% in order to get 30% of a number. Try this one in your head before you read the next paragraph.

What is 40% of 250?

First, find 10% of 250...Now, multiply that by 4. You should have 100.
10% of 250 is 25 and 25 x 4 = 100.

How about that! Did you ever think you could figure out 40% of 250 in your head so quickly? That's why this system works, because now you are looking at numbers logically and becoming a math person!

Now, if you need to figure out 48% of a number, you may not be able to figure it out in your head. You will probably need to write it on paper or use a calculator, but now you know the math that needs to be calculated; just multiply by .48.

Of course, 48% is so close to 50%, you could easily estimate 48% by figuring 50% in your head. Remember 50% is half of anything, so you don't need to find 10% and then multiply by 5. Just cut the number in half. For example, 48% of 600 is figured like this:

$$
\begin{array}{r}
600 \\
\times\ .48 \\
\hline
4800 \\
\underline{24000} \\
28800
\end{array}
$$

Move the decimal over...48% of 600 = 288.00

However, I know that 50% of 600 is 300, so I could have just estimated. I would have said 48% of 600 is a little less than 300 and I'd only be off by 12. Try some on your own.

WORKSHEET 2-18

Use my method to find 20% of the following numbers. First, move the decimal point over one space, then double that number to get 20%.

1. 400
2. 300
3. 50
4. 100
5. 800

6. What is 10% of 200?
7. What is 20% of 300?
8. What is 30% of 400?
9. What is 40% of 100?
10. What is 50% of 220?
11. What is 60% of 300?
12. What is 75% of 320?
13. What is 80% of 800?
14. What is 90% of 1000?
15. What is 100% of a million?

16. The sign says all shoes are 40% off. The original price for the shoes you want to buy is $35.00. How much will the shoes cost during the sale?
17. Stephen went to a restaurant. The total price for dinner was $75.00. Stephen left a 20% tip. How much was the tip?
18. Eric painted his motorcycle helmet 3 different colors. There is green paint on 25% of the helmet. There is yellow paint on 50% of the helmet. What percentage of the helmet is white?
19. Mike bought a guitar at 50% off the regular price. The regular price was $299.00. Approximately how much did Mike spend on his guitar?

LESSON 19: REPLACING WORDS WITH MATH SYMBOLS

How did you do? If you missed more than two on the last worksheet, then read the last lesson over again. It doesn't take long to read and you will be able to learn more the second time around.

In the last lesson you learned how to logically find 10% or 30% of a number in your head. That's easy. But can you solve a problem like this next one?

What is 13% of 23?

This one is a little more challenging. My logical way of figuring this one out would be more difficult than just doing the math. Do you know what math to do? One way to solve this problem is by replacing the words, "what, is, and of" into math symbols. I'll show you what I mean below.

- Replace "what" with a question mark.
- Replace "is" with an equal sign.
- Replace "of" with a multiplication sign.
- Convert 13% into a decimal number (think money).

What is 13% of 23?

↓ ↓ ↓ ↓ ↓

?   =   .13   x   23

Now it is easy to see the math you need to do. I'll rearrange them in a more familiar order and do the math, 23 x .13 = 2.99. This may not seem helpful to you right now, but as the math problems get more difficult, you will come to rely on this trick. All you need to remember are the 3 words and their math symbols:

What → ?

Is ⟶ =

Of ⟶ x

It is easy to remember the first word/symbol: "What = ?" The word "what" is normally followed by a question mark, so they kind of go together. You could also change the phrase, "how much" into a question mark too.

You can remember the word "is" means "=" by thinking: *and the answer is...*

The last word on the list is "of." It means to multiply. Read the following examples of how I can turn everyday sentences into math problems.

If I sell my crafts online, I have to pay 7% of my sales to the website. If my sales are $400.00, how much do I have to pay?

7% of $400.00
↓ ↓ ↙
.07 x $400 = $28

The test had 125 questions on it. I have to get at least 82% of the questions right to pass. How many questions do I have to get right?

82% of 125 is what?
↓ ↙ ↓ ↓
.82 x 125 = 102.5

The classroom normally has 35 children in it, but today 20% of the children were absent. How many children were absent?

What is 20% of 35?
↓ ↓ ↓ ↙
? = .20 x 35

7 = .20 x 35

Try this trick yourself. Complete the next worksheet.

WORKSHEET 2-19

1. What is 33% of 154?
2. 62% of 38 is what?
3. How much is 23% of 55?
4. What is 93% of 18?
5. What is 42% of 9?
6. I received 80% of the 1,045 votes. How many votes did I get?

7. Courtney was reading the reviews of 2 different video games. The first game, Flip-Flop, reported that 85% of the 432 people who played the game, liked it. The review of the other game, Tisk-Task, reported that 97% of the 40 people who played it, liked it. How many people liked each game? You will need to round your answer to the nearest whole number.

8. Chris received a paycheck of $759.00. Here is how he spent it:

   15% was spent on his car, gas, and insurance.
   25% was spent on groceries.
   30% was put towards rent.
   10% went into his savings account.

   How much did he spend on each item above? What percentage of his check does he have left?

9. Cammy wanted to buy a pair of shoes. The brown shoes were regularly $42.00, but she had a coupon for 15% off the regular price. The black pair of shoes were regularly priced at $54.00, but they were on sale for 30% off the regular price. Which pair of shoes cost less?

Name: _____   Date: _____

CHAPTER 2 REVIEW TEST

1.   Fill in the empty boxes below making each row equal.

Decimal	Fraction	Percentage
.02		2%
.20	$\frac{1}{5}$	
.5		
		99%
	$\frac{33}{100}$	
.18		
1.10		

2.   How much money is in the picture? Write your answer as a decimal number, a fraction, and as a percentage of a dollar.

_____   _____   _____

Decimal Number   Fraction   Percentage of a Dollar

3. What is 14% of 50?

4. How much is 29% of 600?

5. How much is 20% of 200?

6. How many decimal points are in the number one million, six-hundred thousand?

7. An hour is 60 minutes. How much is 20% of an hour?

8. What is 400% of 62?

9. 50 people showed up to the concert. 100% of the people were wearing the band's T-shirts. How many people were wearing the T-shirts?

10. Senior Citizens get 15% off on Wednesdays. Anita is a senior citizen and on Wednesday she saved $15 dollars. Can you logically figure out how much Anita's items would have been without the discount?

11. Kahlum's monthly cell phone bill showed that he sent a total of 2,316 text messages. Annabelle received about 45% of the messages and Nina received around 33% of them. The rest of the messages were sent to Trent. Fill in the number of text messages each person received from Kahlum.

    Annabelle: _____
    Nina: _____
    Trent: _____

Check your answers. If you got more than 2 wrong, read chapter 2 again.

CHAPTER 3
NEGATIVE AND POSITIVE NUMBERS

LESSON 20: ADDING NEGATIVE NUMBERS

First of all, let me explain what it means to have a negative number. A nice warm day is somewhere around 80 degrees outside. A cold, winter day is closer to 20 degrees outside. Imagine if it were so cold, that it got down to 0 degrees outside; now that's cold! Now imagine that it got even colder, maybe 10 degrees *below* zero. That's what a negative number is; less than zero. A positive number is any number that is more than zero.

A negative number will be written with a minus sign in front of it. A positive number has a plus sign or no sign at all in front of it. For example, look at the numbers below. They are "negative five," "positive seven," "negative one hundred," and "positive eight."

$$-5 \quad +7 \quad -100 \qquad 8$$

As a rule of thumb, if there is no + sign or - sign in front of a number, it is assumed to be positive, but a negative number will ALWAYS have a minus sign in front of it.

OK, so let's get started. You know that 5 – 5 = 0, so how much is 5 – 6 = ? It is less than 0, isn't it? How much less than 0? 1 less than 0. We call that negative 1 and it is written like this -1.

Look at the next problem. It is a little number minus a larger number.

$$25 - 100 =$$

To solve a problem like the one above, I like to look at it backwards. I'll show you what I mean. I am going to move the equal sign to the front of the problem and then read it backwards.

$$= 25 - 100$$

← ———————————

Now it reads, 100 minus 25. Well that's easy; it's 75. But wait, it's not positive 75, it is NEGATIVE 75.

$$25 - 100 = -75$$

Look at the five problems below. Try to solve them by reading the problems backwards. The first one will be read 10 minus 4 and the answer will be a negative number. Do you know the answer now?

$$4 - 10 = \qquad 7 - 10 = \qquad 5 - 8 = \qquad 12 - 14 = \qquad 100 - 115 =$$

The answers are -6, -3, -3, -2, and -15.

Did you get all the answers right? Just remember, when you see a small number minus a larger number, the answer will always be negative. And the easiest way to solve it is to read it backwards and add a minus sign to the answer. That should be easy to remember because a small number minus a larger number HAS TO be negative.

Now we will move on to adding a positive number and a negative number together. We all know 3 + 3 = 6 because, of course, if you have $3 and you get $3 more, you will have $6. That is a positive number plus a positive number, and of course, we get a positive answer.

Now let's throw in a negative number. The next problem is read, "seven plus negative two."

$$7 + -2 =$$

Think of the positive 7 as \$7 in your hand and the negative 2 as \$2 you owe your sister. If you combine the \$7 dollars in your hand with the \$2 you owe your sister, you really only have 5 dollars total. So the answer is 5.

$$7 + -2 = 5.$$

Let's try another one.

$$8 + -10 = -2$$

Again, you have 8 dollars (the positive number) in your hand, but you owe 10 dollars (the negative number) to your mom. When you combine them, you still owe your mom 2 more dollars, so you have negative 2 dollars.

Consider all positive numbers as money you have in your hand and all negative numbers as money you owe to someone.

Let's try another one.

$$-52 + 53 =$$

You owe your mom \$52, that's the negative number. You get a paycheck for \$53, that's the positive number. Once you pay back your mom, how much money will you have left? That's right, \$1.

If that confuses you, there is another way to look at that last problem. When I look at the problem below, I see two numbers. I see negative 52 and positive 53. I will separate them so you can see each one.

$$-52 + 53 =$$

-52   +53

110

Our job is to combine those two numbers. I say "combine," instead of add or subtract, because it's hard to say if we are adding or subtracting, so we just say "combine."

As long as I don't change the sign in front of each number, I can switch those two numbers around to try and create an easier problem to solve. If I put the positive number first, it will be just like a simple subtraction problem. I can even drop the positive sign, if I want to.

$$\swarrow$$
$$+53 - 52$$

Now the problem reads, 53 minus 52. That's easy, it's 1.

Let's try another one like that because you are going to use negative and positive numbers A LOT in the next book. Look at the problem below.

$$+20 - 30 =$$

When I look at this one, I see twenty dollars minus 30 dollars. So I think to myself, I have $20 in my hand and I owe $30. How much money do I have after paying what I owe? I have negative $10.

$$\searrow$$
$$+20 - 30 = -10$$

You also could have solved this one by reading it backwards. I'll drop the positive sign, so it isn't so funny looking.

$$= 20 - 30$$
$$\longleftarrow$$

Now the problem is 30 minus 20, and we know the answer will be negative, otherwise, we wouldn't bother solving it backwards.

Let's try a few more together. We will decide the best way to solve each one. Look at the next problem.

$$-100 + 90 =$$

Well let's see...reading it backwards doesn't really help me. I could separate the two numbers, making sure I don't change the signs, and then switch them around.

$$-100 \qquad +90$$

$$90 - 100 =$$

That makes it a little more clearly to me and I could solve it backwards now. But I think the best way to solve this one is to look at it as money. The negative 100 represents $100 that I owe. The positive 90 is money I receive. When I combine those two amounts, how much do I still owe?

$$-100 + 90 = -10$$

Here is another one. The problem below is read 45 plus negative 45.

$$45 + -45 =$$

Mmm...reading it backwards doesn't make it look any easier. Switching the two numbers around doesn't help me either. Let's try the money trick. I have $45 in my hand and I owe $45. When we add those two numbers together, I'm out of money, so the answer is 0.

The lesson to be learned here is that anytime you have to ADD a negative number, it is the same thing as subtracting.

$$45 + -45 = \qquad \text{is the same thing as} \qquad 45 - 45 =$$

Now let's add two negative numbers together.

$$-8 + -12 = -20$$

You owe your mom $8 and you owe your sister $12; you owe a total of $20. Something we like to call negative 20 dollars.

Sometimes it is written like this:

$$(-8) + (-12) = (-20)$$

In this situation the parentheses are just there to make it easier to read. Sometimes it helps to separate the plus and minus signs with parentheses. Either way the answer is still -20.

Adding negative and positive numbers is simple, if you just think of the positive numbers as money you have and the negative numbers as money you owe. Put them together and how much money you have left is the answer.

Even if the numbers are fractions, the rules are the same. Look at the problem below.

$$-\frac{3}{8} + -\frac{4}{8} =$$

The math to be solved here is -3 + - 4. If you owe 3 bucks to your mom and 4 bucks to your dad, you owe a total of 7 dollars. The answer is $-\frac{7}{8}$.

Try some on your own on the next worksheet.

WORKSHEET 2-20

1.   14 + -10 =
2.   -15 + 30 =
3.   -40 + -40 =
4.   (-10) + (-20) =
5.   -45 + 25 =
6.   100 + -50 =
7.   -35 + -35 =
8.   25 + 25 =
9.   -25 + 25 =
10.   +30 + -60 =

11.   Sherry owes Mike $500. She owes Eric $600. How much money does Sherry have now?

12.   Stephen gave Logan $25.00. Logan owes his mom $38.00. How much money does Logan have now?

13.   Kaylie received $55.00 for babysitting. She owes her brother $5.00 and she owes her sister $8.00. How much money does Kaylie have now?

14.   My bank account had $17.00 in it yesterday. I just went to the ATM and took out$40.00. How much money is in my bank account now?

15.   Yesterday, the temperature in Alaska was 7 degrees. Today it is 5 degrees below zero. How much colder is it today than yesterday?

16.   Tia owes her dad $10.00 and she owes her brother $6.00. How much money does Tia have?

LESSON 21: SUBTRACTING NEGATIVE AND POSITIVE NUMBERS

We will start off simple.

$$15 - 5 = 10$$

You already know this. If you have positive $15 and you give your brother positive $5, you will be left with positive $10.

Now it gets a little trickier, but don't worry. I can make it simple.

$$10 - -5 = 15$$

You could translate this into money, but it's a little confusing to say you have 10 dollars and you take away a debt you owed your dad, so now you have $15...that doesn't really help us visualize the problem.

The easiest way to solve a problem that has "minus a negative number" is to change the two "minus" signs into two "addition" signs. For example, 10 - -5 is turned into 10 + +5. Now you have simple addition, 10 + 5.

Just remember, when you see "- -" draw a vertical line through both of the minus signs to create a "+ +". This is one time when two negatives do make a positive...but only in math.

Here is another one.

$$-15 - -6 =$$

change it to ++ by drawing 2 lines

$$-15 + +6 =$$

Now just apply the addition rule. You owe 15 dollars and you receive $6; you now have a grand total of negative 9 dollars.

Now we'll try a negative number minus a positive number.

$$-15 - 5 = -20$$

This problem could also be written as (-15) - (+5) = (-20). It's the same thing! So, the negative 15 is money you owe and then someone comes along and takes away (subtracts) another 5 bucks from your bank account. You now have negative $20 in your account.

Remember, a "- - " (negative, negative) should always be turned into a "+ +" (positive, positive). Even if the numbers are fractions, the rules are the same. Look at the problem below.

$$-\frac{2}{9} - -\frac{5}{9} =$$

This problem has a "negative, negative," so turn those signs into "positive, positive" signs.

$$-\frac{2}{9} + +\frac{5}{9} =$$

You can drop one of the positive signs because you can't get any more positive than positive. Now, all you need to solve is -2 + 5. You owe 2 dollars, you receive 5 dollars. How much do you have now? That's right, 3 dollars.

$$-\frac{2}{9} + \frac{5}{9} = \frac{3}{9}$$

Complete the next worksheet. If you don't get 100%, read this section one more time, a little slower, and try again.

WORKSHEET 2-21

1.   80 - -20 =
2.   -40 - 20 =
3.   -10 - -10 =
4.   -25 - -5 =
5.   100 - -5 =
6.   100 - 50 =
7.   -100 - -80 =
8.   -10 - 5 =
9.   -25 - 25 =
10. -32 - -104 =

11. $-\dfrac{7}{8} + -\dfrac{1}{8} =$

12. $\dfrac{7}{12} - -\dfrac{2}{24} =$

13. $-\dfrac{2}{5} - -\dfrac{4}{15} =$

14. $-\dfrac{2}{9} + \dfrac{1}{2} =$

15. $-4\dfrac{3}{5} - 2\dfrac{1}{3} =$

16. $5\dfrac{1}{2} + -2\dfrac{4}{7} =$

17. $-3\dfrac{5}{8} - -3 =$

18. $-.03 + -.63 =$

If you made any mistakes, learn from them or read this chapter again. You shouldn't continue unless you understand adding and subtracting negative and positive numbers completely.

LESSON 22: MULTIPLYING NEGATIVE NUMBERS

There are only two things you need to remember in order to multiply negative and positive numbers together.

- Multiply the two numbers as usual. If the two signs are different, the answer will always be negative.
- If the two signs are the same, the answer will always be positive.

Let me explain:

$$8 \times 8 = 64 \text{ and}$$
$$-8 \times -8 = 64$$

"How can this be?" you ask. I will try to explain, but remember, all you need to know are the two rules listed above. But for those of you who need to know "why," read on.

We know that $8 \times 8 = 64$ because if you have 8 people and they each have $8, together they have $64. That's simple. So if you have 8 people who each owe $8, collectively they have -64 dollars. That math equation would be written as:

$$-8 \times 8 = -64$$

But when we multiply "negative eight" by "negative eight," it is the opposite of multiplying by positive eight, so the answer is positive 64. Make sense? It doesn't have to make sense, just remember the 2 rules above. Here's another example.

$$10 \times -5 =$$

First, you multiply as usual $10 \times 5 = 50$. Then look at the signs; positive 10 and negative 5. They are different signs, so the answer has to be negative.

$$10 \times -5 = -50$$

To recap:

- Same signs = positive answer
- Different signs = negative answer
- It's just that simple.

Here is a way to remember this. When the signs are the same, everything is great, the answer is positive. When the signs are different, they don't agree, the answer is negative.

If you are smiling because you are enjoying your new knowledge, continue on to the next lesson. If you are ready to quit because you don't get it yet, read this lesson again. It won't take long and trust me, negative numbers aren't going away; they will show up in all future math.

Try some on your own, by completing the next worksheet. Be sure to check your answers with the ones in the back of the book.

Name: _____   Date: _____

WORKSHEET 2-22

1. $-3 \times 3 =$
2. $5 \times -5 =$
3. $-7 \times -2 =$
4. $8 \times -5 =$
5. $-9 \times -6 =$
6. $10 \times -3 =$
7. $-4 \times -6 =$
8. $-1 \times -1 =$
9. $-2 \times 1 =$
10. $-3 \times 8 =$

11. $\frac{1}{3} \times -\frac{1}{4} =$

12. $-\frac{3}{5} \times \frac{5}{6} =$

13. $-1\frac{3}{7} \times -3\frac{1}{4} =$

14. $-6 \times \frac{5}{8} =$

15. $-3\frac{7}{8} \times -5 =$

16. $3\frac{3}{4} \times -4\frac{1}{2} =$

17. $-1.55 \times 7.2 =$

18. $-3.007 \times -6.4 =$

19. $9.1 \times -.05 =$

If you feel you have learned negative and positive numbers well enough that you could now teach it to someone else, then move on. Otherwise, do yourself a favor and start over. If you are confused now, you shouldn't continue. You should start over; the second time is always easier.

LESSON 23: DIVIDING NEGATIVE AND POSITIVE NUMBERS

Good news! You already know how to divide negative and positive numbers. It's just like multiplication.

Here are the two rules for division:

- Divide as usual. If the two numbers in the division problem have the same sign (they agree), the answer will be positive.
- If the two numbers in the division problem have different signs (they don't agree), the answer will be negative.

Look at the next problem.

$$-9 \div -3 = 3$$

Divide as usual. 9 divided by 3 = 3. Now look at the signs. The signs are the same, they agree with each other, so the answer is positive. Let's try another one.

$$40 \div -5 = -8$$

Since the signs on the 40 and the 5 are different, they don't agree. The answer has to be negative. Divide as usual and put a negative sign in front of the answer. Do you see how this is the same as multiplication?

Name: _____ Date: _____

WORKSHEET 2-23

1. $10 \div -5 =$

2. $-56 \div -7 =$

3. $-49 \div 7 =$

4. $64 \div -8 =$

5. $28 \div -4 =$

6. $-81 \div -9 =$

7. $36 \div -2 =$

8. $-48 \div -8 =$

9. $-144 \div -12 =$

10. $44 \div 11 =$

11. $-\frac{2}{3} \div -\frac{4}{5} =$

12. $1\frac{1}{4} \div -\frac{1}{3} =$

13. $-3\frac{1}{8} \div -2\frac{4}{8} =$

14. Mick had some custom T-shirts made for his band. The shirts cost $96.00. Mick and the band only saved up $78 for the shirts. After he pays for the shirts, how much money will the band have?

CHAPTER 3 REVIEW TEST

1. $-9 + 14 =$ 2. $-43 + -81 =$ 3. $90 + -45 =$

4. $-1.05 + 9.6 =$ 5. $-\dfrac{3}{5} + -\dfrac{2}{10} =$ 6. $432 - 987 =$

7. $-17 - -5 =$ 8. $-23 - 14 =$ 9. $104 - 16 =$

10. $-4\dfrac{1}{2} - -3\dfrac{1}{3} =$ 11. $5\dfrac{1}{8} - -2\dfrac{1}{4} =$ 12. $.023 - 5.2 =$

13. $-5 \times 8 =$ 14. $7 \times -3 =$ 15. $-10 \times -90 =$

16. $\dfrac{7}{8} \times -\dfrac{5}{6} =$ 17. $32.16 \times -3 =$ 18. $-14 \times \dfrac{1}{2} =$

19. $-75 \div -3 =$ 20. $-150 \div 2 =$ 21. $56 \div -7 =$

22. $\dfrac{7}{12} \div -\dfrac{2}{3} =$ 23. $-\dfrac{6}{24} \div -\dfrac{18}{24} =$ 24. $-1008 \div 9\dfrac{3}{9} =$

25. Keep track of Melodee's money. She received $100 for her birthday. She spent $41.39 at the store. She went to the gas station and spent $44.91 putting gas in her car. She received $25.00 for babysitting and gave her little brother $5.00 for washing her car. How much money does Melodee have left?

Name: _____   Date: _____

FINAL TEST

Solve the following fraction problems. Reduce your answers to the smallest denominator possible and convert any improper fractions into mixed numbers.

1. $2\frac{3}{8} + 3\frac{19}{24} =$

2. $4\frac{3}{7} - 5\frac{4}{8} =$

3. $6\frac{3}{4} \times -7\frac{1}{4} =$

4. $-4\frac{1}{12} \div -\frac{21}{36} =$

5. Which fraction is bigger? Cross multiply and then use a $<$ *or* $>$ sign.

$$\frac{32}{44} \quad \text{---} \quad \frac{48}{55}$$

6. Chris bought a bag of chocolate candies. The bag had 20 pieces of candy in it. Chris gave Nick 5 of the pieces and he gave Tony 8 of the pieces.

a. Write a fraction that shows how much of the bag he gave to Nick.
b. Write a percentage to show how much of the bag he gave to Tony.
c. Write a decimal number to show how much of the candy Chris has left. (Hint: write a fraction and then divide the numbers).

FINAL TEST page 2

7.   Fill in the empty box to make all values equal.

Decimal number	Fraction	Percentage
	$\dfrac{26}{26}$	

Find the arrow and name the measurement:

8.

9.

10.

11.

FINAL TEST page 3

12.   Jessi wants to fill a baby bottle for Annabelle. The directions say to use 1 fluid ounce of the powdered mix and 8 fluid ounces of water. Jessi only has a tablespoon to use for measuring. How many tablespoons of each ingredient should Jessi use?

13.   Name 4 units of measurement used to measure length. Arrange them in order from smallest to biggest.

14.   Name 7 units of measurement used to measure liquids or space. Arrange them in order from smallest to biggest.

15.   Name 3 units of measurement used to measure weight. Arrange them in order from the smallest to biggest.

16.   What is 30% of 12?

17.   What is 23% of 90?

18.   Stephen sells used cars. Every time he sells a car, he earns 12% of the price of the car. Stephen sold a car for $7,225. How much will he be paid?

19.   Many lawn mowers run with gas and oil mixed together. The directions say to mix the gas and oil at a rate of 32 to 1. That means you need to add 1 unit of oil for every 32 units of gas. Sherry wants to add oil to 1 quart of gas. How much oil should she add?

If you got 100% correct on the Final Test, congratulations you are ready for pre-algebra. If you missed more than 2, I strongly encourage you to read this chapter again. Or at least learn from your mistakes.

If you understand everything in this book, you are ready to read Volume 3. If you are a little unclear, read this book again. It will go quickly and you will have a better understanding of math.

ANSWERS

The following pages contain the answers to all worksheets and tests. Be sure to check your answers upon completion. If you get more than 2 incorrect answers, read the lesson again and find out why.

ANSWERS: WORKSHEET 2-1

1. Which of the following are fractions?

   36   42.9 $\left(\dfrac{2}{5}\right)$ 0 $\left(\dfrac{1}{100}\right)$

2. A dime is $\dfrac{1}{10}$ of a dollar and a quarter is $\dfrac{1}{4}$ of a dollar. Can you write a fraction for one penny? $\dfrac{1}{100}$

3. What does the number on the bottom of a fraction mean?
   It is how many pieces it takes to make one.

4. Give a number that is equal to $\dfrac{25}{25}$ **= 1**

5. Write a fraction that equals 2 dimes. $\dfrac{2}{10}$

6. Write the fraction that represents the picture below.

    $\dfrac{75}{100}$ *or* $\dfrac{3}{4}$

7. Write a fraction that equals 1.
   Any fraction that has the same number on top and bottom equals 1.

8. I bought a pack of gum. There were 10 pieces in the pack. I gave my sister 3 of the pieces. Write a fraction that shows how much gum I have left in the pack. $\dfrac{7}{10}$

9. Which fraction is bigger? Use a $<$ *or* $>$ sign.
   $$\dfrac{1}{4} \; > \; \dfrac{1}{100}$$

10. Write a fraction that stands for 3 cents. $\dfrac{3}{100}$

Add the following fractions.

1. $\dfrac{3}{8} + \dfrac{3}{8} = \dfrac{6}{8}$

2. $\dfrac{5}{21} + \dfrac{9}{21} = \dfrac{14}{21}$

3. $\dfrac{1}{4} + \dfrac{2}{4} = \dfrac{3}{4}$

4. $\dfrac{3}{10} + \dfrac{4}{10} = \dfrac{7}{10}$

5. $\dfrac{5}{12} + \dfrac{4}{12} = \dfrac{9}{12}$

6. $\dfrac{1}{5} + \dfrac{3}{5} = \dfrac{4}{5}$

7. $\dfrac{8}{32} + \dfrac{18}{32} = \dfrac{26}{32}$

8. $\dfrac{3}{6} + \dfrac{3}{6} = \dfrac{6}{6} = 1$

9. $\dfrac{4}{16} + \dfrac{7}{16} = \dfrac{11}{16}$

10. $\dfrac{3}{14} + \dfrac{5}{14} = \dfrac{8}{14}$

11. $\dfrac{11}{44} + \dfrac{11}{44} = \dfrac{22}{44}$

12. $\dfrac{3}{27} + \dfrac{4}{27} = \dfrac{7}{27}$

13. $\dfrac{2}{9} + \dfrac{4}{9} = \dfrac{6}{9}$

14. $\dfrac{18}{48} + \dfrac{16}{48} = \dfrac{34}{48}$

15. $\dfrac{4}{15} + \dfrac{3}{15} = \dfrac{7}{15}$

16. $\dfrac{8}{24} + \dfrac{4}{24} = \dfrac{12}{24}$

17. 1/4 + 2/4 = 3/4

18. 3/12 + 4/12 = 7/12

19. 4/10 + 2/10 =6/10

20. 1/3 + 2/3 = 3/3

21. 5/16 + 3/16 = 8/16

22. 3/8 + 3/8 = 6/8

23. 3/7 + 2/7 = 5/7

24. 6/32 + 8/32 = 14/32

25. 7/14 + 2/14 = 9/14

ANSWERS: WORKSHEET 2-3

1. Circle the fraction that is equal to $\frac{1}{2}$.

   $\frac{4}{6}$ $\frac{6}{6}$ $\left(\frac{3}{6}\right)$ $\frac{2}{6}$

2. Which fraction is a bigger amount? Use a $<$ *or* $>$ sign.

   $$\frac{9}{10} > \frac{3}{10}$$

3. Write a math problem using fractions that means "four eighths plus three eighths."

   $$\mathbf{\frac{4}{8} + \frac{3}{8}}$$

4. I have a deck of cards. One deck has 52 cards. I want to separate the cards into 4 equal piles. Write a fraction that shows how much of the deck is in each pile.

   $$\mathbf{52 \div 4 = 13} \qquad \mathbf{\frac{13}{52}}$$

5. I have one dozen eggs. One dozen is 12 eggs. I cooked 5 of the eggs. Write a fraction that shows how much of the dozen is left.

   $$\mathbf{\frac{7}{12}}$$

6. Look at the fraction below. Which number is the denominator? **8**

   $$\frac{3}{8}$$

7. Look at the fraction above. Which number is the numerator? **3**

132

ANSWERS: WORKSHEET 2-4

1. $\dfrac{2}{5} + \dfrac{3}{10} = \dfrac{7}{10}$

2. $\dfrac{3}{8} + \dfrac{3}{24} = \dfrac{12}{24}$

3. $\dfrac{5}{12} + \dfrac{3}{6} = \dfrac{11}{12}$

4. $\dfrac{2}{4} + \dfrac{3}{8} = \dfrac{7}{8}$

5. $\dfrac{5}{22} + \dfrac{1}{11} = \dfrac{7}{22}$

6. $\dfrac{8}{14} + \dfrac{1}{7} = \dfrac{10}{14}$

7. $\dfrac{2}{3} + \dfrac{1}{4} = \dfrac{11}{12}$

8. $\dfrac{1}{5} + \dfrac{1}{2} = \dfrac{7}{10}$

9. $\dfrac{1}{4} + \dfrac{7}{16} = \dfrac{11}{16}$

10. $\dfrac{2}{7} + \dfrac{2}{3} = \dfrac{20}{21}$

11. In January Josh grew three eighths of an inch. In February he grew one fourth of an inch. How much did he grow all together in those two months?
$$\dfrac{3}{8} + \dfrac{1}{4} = \dfrac{5}{8} \text{ of an inch}$$

12. Write and solve a math problem using fractions to add one dime and seven pennies. $\dfrac{1}{10} + \dfrac{7}{100} = \dfrac{17}{100}$

13. Carrie ate five eighths of the pizza. Anita ate six sixteenths of the pizza. Is there any pizza left? $\dfrac{5}{8} + \dfrac{6}{16} = \dfrac{16}{16}$ *No, there is no pizza left.*

14. Which fraction is bigger? Use a $<$ or $>$ sign. $\dfrac{2}{100} < \dfrac{7}{8}$

ANSWERS: WORKSHEET 2-4.5

1. $\dfrac{4}{9} + \dfrac{2}{6} = \quad \dfrac{8}{18} + \dfrac{6}{18} = \mathbf{\dfrac{14}{18}}$

2. $\dfrac{1}{6} + \dfrac{4}{8} = \quad \dfrac{4}{24} + \dfrac{12}{24} = \mathbf{\dfrac{16}{24}}$

3. $\dfrac{1}{4} + \dfrac{5}{8} = \quad \dfrac{2}{8} + \dfrac{5}{8} = \mathbf{\dfrac{7}{8}}$

4. $\dfrac{5}{12} + \dfrac{3}{8} = \quad \dfrac{10}{24} + \dfrac{9}{24} = \mathbf{\dfrac{19}{24}}$

5. $\dfrac{2}{3} + \dfrac{1}{6} = \quad \dfrac{4}{6} + \dfrac{1}{6} = \mathbf{\dfrac{5}{6}}$

6. $\dfrac{3}{14} + \dfrac{3}{4} = \quad \dfrac{6}{28} + \dfrac{21}{28} = \mathbf{\dfrac{27}{28}}$

7.   Beth ate $\dfrac{3}{8}$ of the pizza and Chris ate $\dfrac{3}{5}$ of it. Is there any pizza left?

     $\dfrac{3}{8} + \dfrac{3}{5} = \quad \dfrac{15}{40} + \dfrac{24}{40} = \mathbf{\dfrac{39}{40}}$ **Yes, there is some pizza left.**

     If they had eaten $\dfrac{40}{40}$ of the pizza, there would not be any left.

ANSWERS: WORKSHEET 2-5

Reduce the following fractions down to the smallest denominator.

1.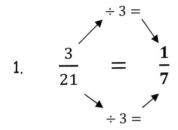
$\dfrac{3}{21} = \dfrac{1}{7}$

$\div 3 =$

$\div 3 =$

2.
$\div 4 =$

$\dfrac{4}{12} = \dfrac{1}{3}$

$\div 4 =$

3. $\dfrac{3}{9} = \dfrac{1}{3}$

4. $\dfrac{50}{100} = \dfrac{1}{2}$

5. $\dfrac{5}{25} = \dfrac{1}{5}$

6. $\dfrac{28}{49} = \dfrac{4}{7}$

Name _____ Date_____

ANSWERS: WORKSHEET 2-5.5

Add the following fractions. Reduce your answers down to the smallest denominator possible.

1. $\dfrac{2}{12} + \dfrac{2}{60} = \dfrac{10}{60} + \dfrac{2}{60} = \dfrac{12}{60} = \dfrac{1}{5}$

2. $\dfrac{2}{8} + \dfrac{4}{6} = \dfrac{6}{24} + \dfrac{16}{24} = \dfrac{22}{24} = \dfrac{11}{12}$

3. $\dfrac{7}{25} + \dfrac{4}{75} = \dfrac{21}{75} + \dfrac{4}{75} = \dfrac{25}{75} = \dfrac{1}{3}$

4. $\dfrac{3}{48} + \dfrac{51}{144} = \dfrac{9}{144} + \dfrac{51}{144} = \dfrac{60}{144} = \dfrac{5}{12}$

5. $\dfrac{2}{11} + \dfrac{11}{121} = \dfrac{22}{121} + \dfrac{11}{121} = \dfrac{33}{121} = \dfrac{3}{11}$

6. List all the factors of 64 and 72 and then circle the Greatest Common Factors.

   64   1, 2, 4, (8) 16, 32, 64

   72   1, 2, 3, 4, 6, (8) 9, 12, 18, 24, 36, 72

7. List 10 multiples of 6 and 8 and then circle the Least Common Multiple.

   6   6, 12, 18, (24) 30, 36, 42, 48, 54, 60

   8   8, 16, (24) 32, 40, 48, 56, 64, 72, 80

ANSWERS: WORKSHEET 2-6

Find each measurement.

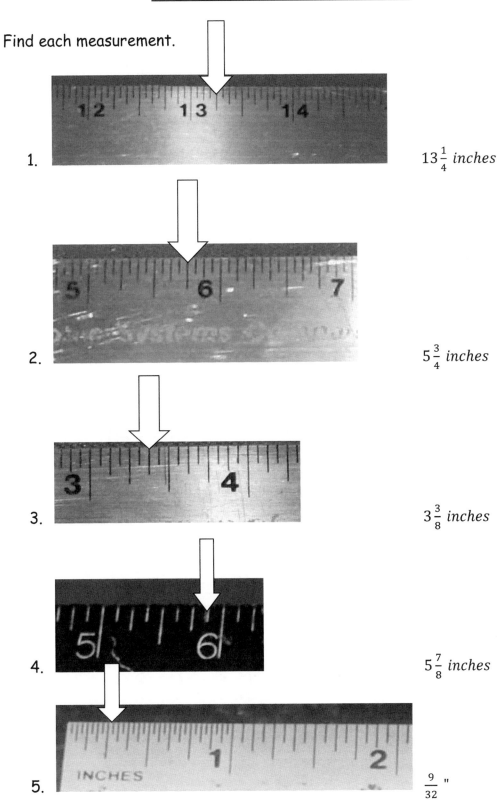

1. $13\frac{1}{4}$ *inches*

2. $5\frac{3}{4}$ *inches*

3. $3\frac{3}{8}$ *inches*

4. $5\frac{7}{8}$ *inches*

5. $\frac{9}{32}$ "

ANSWERS: WORKSHEET 2-7

Subtract the following fractions. If the denominators aren't the same, find a common denominator. Make sure to reduce each of your answers down to the smallest denominator possible.

1. $\dfrac{8}{24} - \dfrac{2}{24} = \dfrac{6}{24} = \dfrac{1}{4}$

2. $\dfrac{9}{36} - \dfrac{3}{36} = \dfrac{6}{36} = \dfrac{1}{6}$

3. $\dfrac{5}{8} - \dfrac{3}{8} = \dfrac{2}{8} = \dfrac{1}{4}$

4. $\dfrac{10}{16} - \dfrac{2}{16} = \dfrac{8}{16} = \dfrac{1}{2}$

5. $\dfrac{12}{32} - \dfrac{4}{32} = \dfrac{8}{32} = \dfrac{1}{4}$

6. $\dfrac{9}{45} - \dfrac{4}{45} = \dfrac{5}{45} = \dfrac{1}{9}$

7. $\dfrac{8}{10} - \dfrac{1}{3} = \dfrac{24}{30} - \dfrac{10}{30} = \dfrac{14}{30} = \dfrac{7}{15}$

8. $\dfrac{3}{4} - \dfrac{1}{5} = \dfrac{15}{20} - \dfrac{4}{20} = \dfrac{11}{20}$

9. $\dfrac{2}{3} - \dfrac{2}{7} = \dfrac{14}{21} - \dfrac{6}{21} = \dfrac{8}{21}$

10. $\dfrac{15}{16} - \dfrac{3}{4} = \dfrac{15}{16} - \dfrac{12}{16} = \dfrac{3}{16}$

11. I drew a line with a big marker. The line was $\frac{1}{4}$ inch wide. I drew another line next to it; making it twice as thick. How thick is the line now?

$\dfrac{1}{4} + \dfrac{1}{4} = \dfrac{2}{4} = \dfrac{1}{2}$ **The line is ½ inch thick.**

12. We planted grass two weeks ago. On Monday, the grass was $\frac{3}{8}$ inches tall. The following Monday, it measured $\frac{15}{16}$ inches tall. How much did the grass grow during that week?

$\dfrac{15}{16} - \dfrac{3}{8} = \dfrac{15}{16} - \dfrac{6}{16} = \dfrac{9}{16}$ **The grass grew 9/16 inch.**

1. $\dfrac{1}{5} + \dfrac{2}{10} = \dfrac{4}{10} = \dfrac{2}{5}$

2. $\dfrac{3}{6} + \dfrac{4}{8} = \dfrac{12}{24} + \dfrac{12}{24} = \dfrac{24}{24} = \mathbf{1}$

3. $\dfrac{1}{4} + \dfrac{6}{8} = \dfrac{8}{8} = \mathbf{1}$

4. $\dfrac{2}{4} + \dfrac{1}{7} = \dfrac{14}{28} + \dfrac{4}{28} = \dfrac{18}{28} = \dfrac{9}{14}$

5. $\dfrac{5}{6} - \dfrac{2\cancel{0}}{12\cancel{0}} = \dfrac{10}{12} - \dfrac{2}{12} = \dfrac{8}{12} = \dfrac{2}{3}$

6. $\dfrac{3}{4} - \dfrac{1}{2} = \dfrac{1}{4}$

7. $\dfrac{4}{7} - \dfrac{2}{8} = \dfrac{32}{56} - \dfrac{14}{56} = \dfrac{18}{56} = \dfrac{9}{28}$

8. $\dfrac{3\cancel{0}}{6\cancel{0}} - \dfrac{2\cancel{0}}{4\cancel{0}} = \dfrac{6}{12} - \dfrac{6}{12} = \mathbf{0}$

9. Tina is making some cookies. The recipe calls for one half cup of sugar. She only has one quarter cup of sugar. How much more sugar does she need to make the cookies? $\dfrac{1}{2} - \dfrac{1}{4} = \dfrac{2}{4} - \dfrac{1}{4} = \dfrac{1}{4}$

    She needs ¼ cup more sugar.

10. Carrie was trying to find one dozen colored eggs. One dozen equals 12 eggs. So far she has found 9 of them. Write a fraction that shows how much of the dozen she has left to find. $\dfrac{3}{12} \; or \; \dfrac{1}{4}$

Cross multiply and then use a $< or >$ sign, to say which fraction is bigger.

11. $\overset{60}{\dfrac{5}{8}} \; > \; \overset{56}{\dfrac{7}{12}}$

12. $\overset{49}{\dfrac{7}{9}} \; < \; \overset{54}{\dfrac{6}{7}}$

13. $\overset{24}{\dfrac{3}{4}} \; = \; \overset{24}{\dfrac{6}{8}}$

    ## They are equal!

ANSWERS: WORKSHEET 2-9

Multiply or divide the following fractions.

1. $\dfrac{4}{8} \times \dfrac{2}{1} = \dfrac{8}{8} = 1$

2. $\dfrac{4}{8} \div \dfrac{2}{1} = \dfrac{4}{8} \times \dfrac{1}{2} = \dfrac{4}{16} = \dfrac{1}{4}$

3. $\dfrac{1}{10} \times \dfrac{5}{1} = \dfrac{5}{10} = \dfrac{1}{2}$

4. $\dfrac{1}{4} \div \dfrac{2}{3} = \dfrac{1}{4} \times \dfrac{3}{2} = \dfrac{3}{8}$

5. $\dfrac{3}{4} \times \dfrac{3}{7} = \dfrac{9}{28}$

6. $\dfrac{2}{6} \div \dfrac{4}{5} = \dfrac{2}{6} \times \dfrac{5}{4} = \dfrac{10}{24} = \dfrac{5}{12}$

7. I stacked up 4 pieces of wood. Each piece is $\frac{1}{8}$ inch thick. How tall is the stack of wood? (one eighth times four) $\dfrac{1}{8} \times \dfrac{4}{1} = \dfrac{4}{8} = \dfrac{1}{2}$ **It is ½" tall.**

8. Divide two fifths by three fourth. $\dfrac{2}{5} \div \dfrac{3}{4} = \dfrac{2}{5} \times \dfrac{4}{3} = \dfrac{8}{15}$

9. Multiply. $\dfrac{3}{5} \times \dfrac{1}{4} = \dfrac{3}{20}$

    Next, divide your answer by $\dfrac{1}{4}$. $\qquad \dfrac{3}{20} \div \dfrac{1}{4} = \dfrac{3}{20} \times \dfrac{4}{1} = \dfrac{12}{20} = \dfrac{3}{5}$

    That answer should be $\dfrac{3}{5}$. **It is!**

To find one half of any number, multiply it by $\dfrac{1}{2}$.

10. How much is one half of $\dfrac{3}{4}$? $\qquad \dfrac{3}{4} \times \dfrac{1}{2} = \dfrac{3}{8}$

11. How much is one half of $\dfrac{7}{8}$? $\qquad \dfrac{7}{8} \times \dfrac{1}{2} = \dfrac{7}{16}$

12. Write and solve a math problem, using fractions, to prove that one half of two is one.

$$\dfrac{2}{1} \times \dfrac{1}{2} = \dfrac{2}{2} = 1$$

ANSWERS: WORKSHEET 2-10

Convert each mixed number into an improper fraction.

1. $4\frac{5}{8} = \frac{37}{8}$

2. $2\frac{3}{4} = \frac{11}{4}$

3. $1\frac{7}{10} = \frac{17}{10}$

4. $6\frac{8}{20} = \frac{128}{20}$

5. $8\frac{1}{3} = \frac{25}{3}$

6. $5\frac{6}{9} = \frac{51}{9}$

7. $3\frac{2}{11} = \frac{35}{11}$

8. $7\frac{1}{5} = \frac{36}{5}$

Convert each improper fraction into a mixed number.

9. $\frac{10}{8} = 1\frac{2}{8}$

10. $\frac{21}{10} = 2\frac{1}{10}$

11. $\frac{22}{7} = 3\frac{1}{7}$

12. $\frac{26}{5} = 5\frac{1}{5}$

13. $\frac{400}{12} = 33\frac{4}{12}$

14. $\frac{386}{3} = 128\frac{2}{3}$

15. $\frac{200}{10} = 20$

16. $\frac{3}{1} = 3$

ANSWERS: WORKSHEET 2-11

Add the following mixed numbers.

1. $5\frac{2}{8} + 4\frac{3}{8} = 9\frac{5}{8}$

2. $2\frac{6}{12} + 6\frac{5}{12} = 8\frac{11}{12}$

3. $3\frac{3}{16} + 3\frac{2}{16} = 6\frac{5}{16}$

4. $5\frac{4}{10} + 3\frac{1}{5} = 8\frac{6}{10} = 8\frac{3}{5}$

5. $4\frac{7}{8} + 3\frac{1}{16} = 7\frac{15}{16}$

6. $18\frac{2}{5} + 3\frac{5}{25} = 21\frac{15}{25} = 21\frac{3}{5}$

7. $7\frac{8}{32} + 5\frac{7}{8} = 12\frac{36}{32} = 13\frac{4}{32} = 13\frac{1}{8}$

8. $11\frac{8}{48} + 9\frac{21}{24} = 20\frac{50}{48} = 21\frac{2}{48} = 21\frac{1}{24}$

9. Jennifer poured $1\frac{1}{2}$ cups of sand into a bucket. Jessi added $\frac{3}{4}$ cups of sand to the bucket. How much sand is in the bucket now?
$$1\frac{1}{2} + \frac{3}{4} = 1\frac{2}{4} + \frac{3}{4} = 1\frac{5}{4} = 2\frac{1}{4} \; cups \; of \; sand$$

10. There are two books stacked up on the table. One book measures $1\frac{7}{8}$ inches. The other book is $1\frac{5}{16}$ inches tall. How tall is the stack of two books?
$$1\frac{7}{8} + 1\frac{5}{16} = 1\frac{14}{16} + 1\frac{5}{16} = 2\frac{19}{16} = 3\frac{3}{16} \; inches$$

11. Pat kicked the ball $36\frac{1}{3}$ feet. Linda kicked the ball $4\frac{3}{4}$ feet farther. How far did Linda kick the ball?
$$36\frac{1}{3} + 4\frac{3}{4} = 36\frac{4}{12} + 4\frac{9}{12} = 40\frac{13}{12} = 41\frac{1}{12} \; feet$$

12. Maggi worked three days last week. On Monday, she worked $5\frac{1}{2}$ hours. On Wednesday, she worked $6\frac{3}{4}$ hours. On Friday, she worked $7\frac{1}{4}$ hours. How many hours did she work last week?
$$5\frac{1}{2} + 6\frac{3}{4} + 7\frac{1}{4} = 18\frac{6}{4} = 19\frac{2}{4} = 19\frac{1}{2} \; hours$$

13. When Debbie got her puppy, he was $7\frac{5}{8}$ inches tall. Since then he has grown $2\frac{3}{4}$ inches more. How tall is the puppy now?
$$7\frac{5}{8} + 2\frac{3}{4} = 9\frac{11}{8} = 10\frac{3}{8} \; inches$$

ANSWERS: WORKSHEET 2-12

Subtract the following mixed numbers.

1. $7\frac{3}{8} - 5\frac{1}{8} = 2\frac{2}{8} = 2\frac{1}{4}$

2. $9\frac{2}{3} - 3\frac{1}{3} = 6\frac{1}{3}$

3. $20\frac{5}{7} - 15\frac{1}{3} = 20\frac{15}{21} - 15\frac{7}{21} = 5\frac{8}{21}$

4. $14\frac{1}{2} - 6\frac{1}{8} = 14\frac{4}{8} - 6\frac{1}{8} = 8\frac{3}{8}$

5. $11\frac{9}{16} - 6\frac{1}{2} = 11\frac{9}{16} - 6\frac{8}{16} = 5\frac{1}{16}$

6. $14\frac{3}{4} - 8\frac{7}{24} = 14\frac{18}{24} - 8\frac{7}{24} = 6\frac{11}{24}$

7. $9\frac{2}{3} - 3\frac{1}{3} = 6\frac{1}{3}$

8. $15\frac{1}{4} - 9\frac{5}{8} = 15\frac{2}{8} - 9\frac{5}{8} = \frac{122}{8} - \frac{77}{8} = \frac{45}{8} = 5\frac{5}{8}$

9. Yesterday there was $4\frac{1}{8}$ inches of rain in the rain gauge. Today it measures $5\frac{3}{16}$ inches of rain. How much did it rain in the last day?

$$5\frac{3}{16} - 4\frac{1}{8} = 5\frac{3}{16} - 4\frac{2}{16} = 1\frac{1}{16} \; inches$$

10. Last year our apple tree was $8\frac{1}{4}$ feet tall. This year the apple tree is $10\frac{1}{2}$ feet tall. How much did the tree grow during the last year?

$$10\frac{1}{2} - 8\frac{1}{4} = 10\frac{2}{4} - 8\frac{1}{4} = 2\frac{1}{4} \; feet$$

11. Linda kicked the ball $44\frac{5}{12}$ feet. Pat kicked the ball $41\frac{1}{12}$ feet. How much farther did Linda kick the ball than Pat?

$$44\frac{5}{12} - 41\frac{1}{12} = 3\frac{4}{12} = 3\frac{1}{3} \; feet$$

12. Teresa added $1\frac{1}{3}$ cups of water to the fish bowl. Now the fish bowl has a total of $22\frac{1}{2}$ cups of water. How much water was in the bowl before Teresa added water?

$$22\frac{1}{2} - 1\frac{1}{3} = 22\frac{3}{6} - 1\frac{2}{6} = 21\frac{1}{6} \; cups \; of \; water$$

13. The first song on the CD was $3\frac{1}{4}$ minutes long. The entire CD was 45 minutes long. How long were the remaining songs?

$$\frac{45}{1} - 3\frac{1}{4} = \frac{180}{4} - \frac{13}{4} = \frac{167}{4} = 41\frac{3}{4} \; minutes$$

ANSWERS: WORKSHEET 2-13

Multiply the following mixed numbers.

1. $\quad 3\dfrac{4}{7} \times 2\dfrac{3}{10} = \dfrac{25}{7} \times \dfrac{23}{10} = \dfrac{575}{70} = 8\dfrac{15}{70} = 8\dfrac{3}{14}$

2. $\quad 2\dfrac{9}{10} \times 4\dfrac{3}{8} = \dfrac{29}{10} \times \dfrac{35}{8} = \dfrac{1015}{80} = 12\dfrac{55}{80} = 12\dfrac{11}{16}$

3. $\quad 4\dfrac{1}{3} \times 3\dfrac{7}{8} = \dfrac{13}{3} \times \dfrac{31}{8} = \dfrac{403}{24} = 16\dfrac{19}{24}$

4. $\quad 10\dfrac{1}{2} \times 3\dfrac{1}{3} = \dfrac{21}{2} \times \dfrac{10}{3} = \dfrac{210}{6} = 35$

5. $\quad 8 \times 3\dfrac{6}{10} = \dfrac{8}{1} \times \dfrac{36}{10} = \dfrac{288}{10} = 28\dfrac{8}{10} = 28\dfrac{4}{5}$

To find one half of any number, multiply it by $\dfrac{1}{2}$.

6. $\quad$ How long is $\dfrac{1}{2}$ of $4\dfrac{5}{8}$ miles? $\qquad 4\dfrac{5}{8} \times \dfrac{1}{2} = \dfrac{37}{8} \times \dfrac{1}{2} = \dfrac{37}{16} = 2\dfrac{5}{16}$ **miles**

7. $\quad$ How much is $\dfrac{1}{2}$ of $\dfrac{1}{2}$? $\qquad \dfrac{1}{2} \times \dfrac{1}{2} = \dfrac{1}{4}$

8. $\quad$ How much is $\dfrac{1}{2}$ of $3\dfrac{7}{8}$? $\qquad 3\dfrac{7}{8} \times \dfrac{1}{2} = \dfrac{31}{8} \times \dfrac{1}{2} = \dfrac{31}{16} = 1\dfrac{15}{16}$

9. $\quad$ I taped 3 small pieces of paper together, to make one long piece. Each piece of paper was $5\dfrac{3}{4}$ inches long. How long is the paper now that the 3 pieces are taped together? $5\dfrac{3}{4} \times \dfrac{3}{1} = \dfrac{23}{4} \times \dfrac{3}{1} = \dfrac{69}{4} = 17\dfrac{1}{4}$ *inches*

10. $\quad$ Sherry wants to put 3 photographs onto 1 page of her scrapbook. Each picture is $2\dfrac{1}{8}$ inches long. The page is 7 inches long. Will all 3 pictures fit on 1 page? $\quad 2\dfrac{1}{8} \times \dfrac{3}{1} = \dfrac{17}{8} \times \dfrac{3}{1} = \dfrac{51}{8} = 6\dfrac{3}{8}$ *Yes they will fit.*

ANSWERS: WORKSHEET 2-14

1. $$2\frac{1}{11} \div 4\frac{5}{8} = \frac{23}{11} \div \frac{37}{8} = \frac{23}{11} \times \frac{8}{37} = \frac{184}{407}$$

2. $$4\frac{4}{9} \div 1\frac{3}{5} = \frac{40}{9} \div \frac{8}{5} = \frac{40}{9} \times \frac{5}{8} = \frac{200}{72} = 2\frac{56}{72} = 2\frac{7}{9}$$

3. $$2\frac{1}{12} \div 3\frac{2}{7} = \frac{25}{12} \div \frac{23}{7} = \frac{25}{12} \times \frac{7}{23} = \frac{175}{276}$$

4. $$3\frac{3}{8} \div 5\frac{2}{9} = \frac{27}{8} \div \frac{47}{9} = \frac{27}{8} \times \frac{9}{47} = \frac{243}{376}$$

5. $$44 \div \frac{3}{11} = \frac{44}{1} \div \frac{3}{11} = \frac{44}{1} \times \frac{11}{3} = \frac{484}{3} = 161\frac{1}{3}$$

To find half of any number, you can divide by 2, or $\frac{2}{1}$.

6. Brianna wants to hang a picture in the center of the wall. The wall measures $8\frac{1}{4}$ feet wide. To find the center of the wall, she needs to find the half way point. What is half of $8\frac{1}{4}$ feet?
$$8\frac{1}{4} \div 2 = \frac{33}{4} \div \frac{2}{1} = \frac{33}{4} \times \frac{1}{2} = \frac{33}{8} = 4\frac{1}{8} feet$$

7. Tia is making some cookies. The recipe will make 48 cookies. Tia only wants to make 24 cookies, so she is only using half the amount of each ingredient. The recipe calls for $2\frac{1}{4}$ cups of flour. How much flour should Tia use?
$$2\frac{1}{4} \div 2 = \frac{9}{4} \div \frac{2}{1} = \frac{9}{4} \times \frac{1}{2} = \frac{9}{8} = 1\frac{1}{8} \ cups \ of \ flour$$

8. Austin wants to make as many plaster molds as he can. Each mold needs $\frac{1}{4}$ cup of plaster. He has $3\frac{3}{4}$ cups of plaster. How many molds can he make?
$$3\frac{3}{4} \div \frac{1}{4} = \frac{15}{4} \div \frac{1}{4} = \frac{15}{4} \times \frac{4}{1} = \frac{60}{4} = 15 \ molds$$

146

ANSWERS: WORKSHEET 2-15

Multiply and divide the following fractions. Cross cancel whenever possible.

1. $\dfrac{\overset{4}{\cancel{8}}}{\underset{2}{\cancel{16}}} \times \dfrac{\overset{1}{\cancel{8}}}{\underset{5}{\cancel{10}}} = \dfrac{4}{10} = \dfrac{2}{5}$

2. $\dfrac{\overset{1}{\cancel{3}}}{\underset{8}{\cancel{48}}} \times \dfrac{\overset{1}{\cancel{6}}}{\underset{7}{\cancel{21}}} = \dfrac{1}{56}$

3. $\dfrac{7}{\underset{2}{\cancel{12}}} \times \dfrac{\overset{1}{\cancel{6}}}{10} = \dfrac{7}{20}$

4. $\dfrac{\overset{1}{\cancel{2}}}{\underset{2}{\cancel{10}}} \times \dfrac{\overset{1}{\cancel{5}}}{\underset{12}{\cancel{24}}} = \dfrac{1}{24}$

5. $\dfrac{8}{56} \div \dfrac{4}{7} = \dfrac{\overset{2}{\cancel{8}}}{\underset{8}{\cancel{56}}} \times \dfrac{\overset{1}{\cancel{7}}}{\underset{1}{\cancel{4}}} = \dfrac{2}{8} = \dfrac{1}{4}$

6. $\dfrac{9}{64} \div \dfrac{3}{8} = \dfrac{\overset{3}{\cancel{9}}}{\underset{8}{\cancel{64}}} \times \dfrac{\overset{1}{\cancel{8}}}{\underset{1}{\cancel{3}}} = \dfrac{3}{8}$

7. $\dfrac{5}{42} \div \dfrac{2}{6} = \dfrac{5}{\underset{7}{\cancel{42}}} \times \dfrac{\overset{1}{\cancel{6}}}{2} = \dfrac{5}{14}$

8. $\dfrac{7}{35} \div \dfrac{1}{7} = \dfrac{7}{\underset{5}{\cancel{35}}} \times \dfrac{\overset{1}{\cancel{7}}}{1} = \dfrac{7}{5} = 1\dfrac{2}{5}$

9. $\dfrac{3}{24} \div \dfrac{3}{6} = \dfrac{\overset{1}{\cancel{3}}}{\underset{4}{\cancel{24}}} \times \dfrac{\overset{1}{\cancel{6}}}{\underset{1}{\cancel{3}}} = \dfrac{1}{4}$

10. $\dfrac{9}{27} \div \dfrac{3}{9} = \dfrac{\overset{3}{\cancel{9}}}{\underset{3}{\cancel{27}}} \times \dfrac{\overset{1}{\cancel{9}}}{\underset{1}{\cancel{3}}} = \dfrac{3}{3} = 1$

ANSWERS: Chapter 1 Review Test

Solve the following problems. Reduce all answers down to the smallest denominator possible. Convert all improper fractions into mixed numbers.

1. $\frac{1}{8} + 2\frac{3}{8} = 2\frac{4}{8} = 2\frac{1}{2}$

2. $3\frac{4}{6} + \frac{1}{5} = 3\frac{20}{30} + \frac{6}{30} = 3\frac{26}{30} = 3\frac{13}{15}$

3. $\frac{5}{8} - \frac{1}{16} = \frac{10}{16} - \frac{1}{16} = \frac{9}{16}$

4. $5\frac{5}{12} - 2\frac{3}{4} = 5\frac{5}{12} - 2\frac{9}{12} = \frac{65}{12} - \frac{33}{12} = \frac{32}{12} = 2\frac{8}{12} = 2\frac{2}{3}$

5. $2\frac{5}{8} \times 3 = \frac{21}{8} \times \frac{3}{1} = \frac{63}{8} = 7\frac{7}{8}$

6. $3\frac{4}{8} \div 4 = \frac{28}{8} \div \frac{4}{1} = \frac{\overset{7}{\cancel{28}}}{8} \times \frac{1}{\underset{1}{\cancel{4}}} = \frac{7}{8}$

7. I have a stack of baseball cards that measures $\frac{1}{2}$ inch high. Your stack of baseball cards is $\frac{1}{8}$ inch taller than mine. How tall is your stack of cards?

    $\frac{1}{2} + \frac{1}{8} = \frac{4}{8} + \frac{1}{8} = \frac{5}{8}$ **Your stack of cards is 5/8 inch tall.**

8. Brendon cut a sandwich into 8 pieces. John ate one of the pieces. How much of a sandwich does he have left?

    $$\frac{7}{8}$$

9. Here is a recipe for 4 dozen cookies. We want to make only 2 dozen, so we need to cut the recipe in half. Rewrite the amounts needed to make half the recipe.

    $2\frac{1}{4}$ Cups of flour $= 2\frac{1}{4} \times \frac{1}{2} = \frac{9}{4} \times \frac{1}{2} = \frac{9}{8} = 1\frac{1}{8}\, cups$

$\frac{3}{4}$ Cup sugar = $\frac{3}{4} \times \frac{1}{2} = \frac{3}{8} cup$

$\frac{1}{2}$ Cup brown sugar = $\frac{1}{2} \times \frac{1}{2} = \frac{1}{4} cup$

$\frac{2}{3}$ Cup butter = $\frac{2}{3} \times \frac{1}{2} = \frac{2}{6} = \frac{1}{3} cup$

2   Eggs = $\frac{2}{1} \times \frac{1}{2} = \frac{2}{2} = 1 \, egg, \, of \, course$

1   Teaspoon baking soda = $\frac{1}{1} \times \frac{1}{2} = \frac{1}{2} \, teaspoon$

$\frac{1}{3}$ Tablespoon salt = $\frac{1}{6} \, tablespoon \, or \, \frac{1}{2} \, teaspoon$

$\frac{1}{4}$ Teaspoon vanilla = $\frac{1}{4} \times \frac{1}{2} = \frac{1}{8} \, teaspoon$

10.   A newspaper costs 8/10 of a dollar. How much does it cost? **80 cents.**

11.   Kathy wants to hang a picture in the center of a wall. The wall measures 37 3/4" wide. She needs to find the center of the wall. Half of 37 3/4" would be the center. How far from the edge of the wall should Kathy measure, to make sure the nail is in the center of the wall?

$$37\frac{3}{4} \times \frac{1}{2} = \frac{151}{4} \times \frac{1}{2} = \frac{151}{8} = 18\frac{7}{8} \textit{ inches from the edge of the wall.}$$

12.   Write a fraction to show what line the arrow is pointing at. $\frac{11}{16} \, inch$

ANSWERS: WORKSHEET 2-16

1. Fill in the blank boxes below.

Fraction	Decimal pt.	Percentage
$\frac{1}{2}$	**.50**	50%
8/10	.80	**80%**
32/100	.32	32%
1/100	**.01**	1%
2/10	.2	**20%**
99/100	.99	99%
7/100	**.07**	**7%**
33/100	.33	**33%**
1/10	**.1**	10%

2. How much is 10% of a dollar? **10 cents**

3. Write 56 cents as a fraction. Reduce your answer. $\frac{56}{100} = \frac{28}{50} = \frac{14}{25}$

4. Write $\frac{1}{2}$ as a decimal number. **.5**

5. There are 342 jelly beans in a jar. 50% of them are blue. How many blue jelly beans are in the jar? **342 x .50 = 171 blue jelly beans**

6. How many years are in a **cent**ury? **100**

7. How many **cent**s are in a dollar? **100**

8. What does the word per**cent** mean? **Per 100**

9. There were 100 people in the room. 99 of them were under the age 70. What percentage of people in the room were over age 70? **1%**

ANSWERS: WORKSHEET 2-17

How much is 10% of:

1. 100 = 10
2. 80 = 8
3. 75 = 7.5
4. 850 = 85
5. 962 = 96.2

How much is 25% of:

6. 100 **25**
7. 12   **3**
8. 40   **10**
9. 200 **50**
10. 16   **4**

11. Write .25 as a fraction. Reduce your answer. $\frac{25}{100} = \frac{1}{4}$

12. Write .50 as a fraction. Reduce your answer. $\frac{50}{100} = \frac{1}{2}$

13. Write one tenth as a percentage.   **10%**

14. How much is 10% of 2,457?   **245.7**

15. How much is 10% of one million?   **100,000**

16. How much is 10% of a dollar?   **10 cents**

17. Judy bought a case of ice tea. There are 10 bottles of tea in each case. She put 20% of them in the refrigerator. How many bottles did Judy put in the refrigerator?   **2 bottles**

18. Daryl went fishing. He caught 40 fish. 50% of the fish weighed over 10 pounds. How many fish weighed less than 10 pounds?   **20 fish**

19. Marion took her dog out for a 2 hour walk. Marion's dog was on the leash 50% of the time. How long was her dog on a leash? **1 hour**

20. Chuck is 70 years old. He has lived in Seattle 50% of his life. How long has he lived in Seattle?   **35 years**

ANSWERS: WORKSHEET 2-18

Use my method to find 20% of the following numbers. First, move the decimal point over one space, then double that number to get 20%.

1. 400   80
2. 300   60
3. 50   10
4. 100   20
5. 800   160

6. What is 10% of 200?   20
7. What is 20% of 300?   60
8. What is 30% of 400?   120
9. What is 40% of 100?   40
10. What is 50% of 220?   110
11. What is 60% of 300?   180
12. What is 75% of 320?   240
13. What is 80% of 800?   640
14. What is 90% of 1000?   900
15. What is 100% of a million? 1,000,000

16. The sign says all shoes are 40% off. The original price for the shoes you want to buy is $35.00. How much will the shoes cost during the sale?   **35 x .4 = 14   35 – 14 = 21 dollars**

17. Stephen went to a restaurant. The total price for dinner was $75.00. Stephen left a 20% tip. How much was the tip?
    $7.50 + $7.50 = $15.00 tip.

18. Eric painted his motorcycle helmet 3 different colors. There was green paint on 25% of the helmet. There was yellow paint on 50% of the helmet. What percentage of the helmet was white?
    25% of the helmet was white.

19. Mike bought a guitar at 50% off the regular price. The regular price was $299.00. Approximately how much did Mike spend on his guitar?
    Approximately $150.00

ANSWERS: WORKSHEET 2-19

1. What is 33% of 154?   ? = .33 × 154   **50.82**
2. 62% of 38 is what?   .62 × 38 = ?   **23.56**
3. How much is 23% of 55? ? = .23 × 55   **12.65**
4. What is 93% of 18?   ? = .93 × 18   **16.74**
5. What is 42% of 9?   ? = .42 × 9   **3.78**
6. I received 80% of the 1,045 votes. How many votes did I get?

   .80 × 1045 = 836 votes

7. Courtney was reading the reviews of 2 different video games. The first game, Flip-Flop, said 85% of the 432 people who played the game liked it. The review of the other game, Tisk-Task, said 97% of the 40 people who played it, liked it. How many people liked each game?

   Flip-Flop: 432 × 85% = 367 people liked it.

   Tisk-Task: 40 × 97% = 39 people liked it.

8. Chris received a paycheck of $759.00. Here is how he spent it:

   15% was spent on his car, gas, and insurance. $759 × .15 = \$113.85$

   25% was spent on groceries. $759 × .25 = \$189.75$

   30% was put towards rent. $759 × .3 = \$227.70$

   10% went into his savings account. $759 × .1 = \$75.90$

   Total spent: $607.20   15% + 25% + 30% + 10% = 80% He has 20% left.

9. Cammy wanted to buy a pair of shoes. The brown shoes were regularly $42.00, but she had a coupon for 15% off the regular price. The black pair of shoes were regularly priced at $54.00, but they were on sale for 30% off the regular price. Which pair of shoes cost less?

   Brown shoes: $42.00 × 15% = $6.30

   ** $42.00 − $6.30 = $35.70**

   Black shoes: $54.00 × 30% = $16.20

   ** $54.00 − $16.20 =$37.80**

   The brown shoes cost less.

ANSWERS: Chapter 2 Review Test

1. Fill in the empty boxes below making each row equal.

Decimal	Fraction	Percentage
.02	$\dfrac{2}{100}$ or $\dfrac{1}{50}$	2%
.20	$\dfrac{1}{5}$	**20%**
.5	$\dfrac{50}{100}$ or $\dfrac{1}{2}$	50%
.99	$\dfrac{99}{100}$	99%
.33	$\dfrac{33}{100}$	**33%**
.18	$\dfrac{18}{100}$ or $\dfrac{9}{50}$	**18%**
1.10	$\dfrac{110}{100}$ or $1\dfrac{1}{10}$	**110%**

2. How much money is in the picture? Write your answer as a decimal number, a fraction, and as a percentage of a dollar.

.75 $\dfrac{75}{100} = \dfrac{3}{4}$ **75%**

Decimal Number   Fraction   Percentage of a Dollar

ANSWERS: Chapter 2 Review Test page 2

3. What is 14% of 50? $? = .14 \times 50$ **7**

4. How much is 29% of 600? $? = .29 \times 600$ **174**

5. How much is 20% of 200? $? = .2 \times 200$ **40**

6. How many decimal points are in the number one million, six-hundred thousand? **One. There can only be one decimal point in any number.**

7. An hour is 60 minutes. How much is 20% of an hour?
   $? = .2 \times 60 =$ **12 minutes**

8. What is 400% of 62? $? = 4 \times 62$ **248**

9. 50 people showed up to the concert. 100% of the people were wearing the band's T-shirts. How many people were wearing the T-shirts? **Everyone – 50 people.**

10. Senior Citizens get 15% off on Wednesdays. Anita is a senior citizen and on Wednesday she saved $15 dollars. Can you logically figure out how much Anita's items would have been without the discount? **$15 is 15% of $100. Anita's items would have cost $100.**

11. Kahlum's monthly cell phone bill showed that he sent a total of 2,316 text messages. Annabelle received about 45% of the messages and Nina received around 33% of them. The rest of the messages were sent to Trent. Fill in the number of text messages each person received from Kahlum.

   Annabelle: 2,316 x 45% = 1042 messages
   Nina: 2,316 x 33% = 764 messages
   Trent: 45% + 33% = 78%   100% - 78% = 22%
   2,316 x 22% = 510

ANSWERS: WORKSHEET 2-20

1. $14 + -10 = 4$
2. $-15 + 30 = 15$
3. $-40 + -40 = -80$
4. $(-10) + (-20) = -30$
5. $-45 + 25 = -20$
6. $100 + -50 = 50$
7. $-35 + -35 = -70$
8. $25 + 25 = 50$
9. $-25 + 25 = 0$
10. $+30 + -60 = -30$

11. Sherry owes Mike $500. She owes Eric $600. How much money does Sherry have now? **$-500 + -600 = - \$1,100$**

12. Stephen gave Logan $25.00. Logan owes his mom $38.00. How much money does Logan have now? **$25 + -38 = -13$**

13. Kaylie received $55.00 for babysitting. She owes her brother $5.00 and she owes her sister $8.00. How much money does Kaylie have now? **$-5 + -8 = -13$**   **$55 - 13 = \$42.00$**

14. My bank account had $17.00 in it yesterday. I just went to the ATM and took out$40.00. How much money is in my bank account now? **$17 - 40 = -23.00$ dollars**

15. Yesterday, the temperature in Alaska was 7 degrees. Today it is 5 degrees below zero. How much colder is it today than yesterday? **$7 - - 5 = 12$ degrees colder**

16. Tia owes her dad $10.00 and she owes her brother $6.00. How much money does Tia have? **$-10 + - 6 = -16$ dollars**

156

ANSWERS: WORKSHEET 2-21

1. 80 - -20 = 100
2. -40 - 20 = -60
3. -10 - -10 = 0
4. -25 - -5 = -20
5. 100 - -5 = 105
6. 100 - 50 = 50
7. -100 - -80 = -20
8. -10 - 5 = -15
9. -25 - 25 = -50
10. -32 - -104 = 72

11. $-\frac{7}{8} + -\frac{1}{8} = -\frac{8}{8} = -1$

12. $\frac{7}{12} - -\frac{2}{24} = \frac{14}{24} + \frac{2}{24} = \frac{16}{24} = \frac{2}{3}$

13. $-\frac{2}{5} - -\frac{4}{15} = -\frac{6}{15} + \frac{4}{15} = -\frac{2}{15}$

14. $-\frac{2}{9} + \frac{1}{2} = -\frac{4}{18} + \frac{9}{18} = \frac{5}{18}$

15. $-4\frac{3}{5} - 2\frac{1}{3} = -4\frac{9}{15} - 2\frac{5}{15} = -6\frac{14}{15}$

16. $5\frac{1}{2} + -2\frac{4}{7} = 5\frac{7}{14} - 2\frac{8}{14} = \frac{77}{14} - \frac{36}{14} = \frac{41}{14} = 2\frac{13}{14}$

17. $-3\frac{5}{8} - -3 = -3\frac{5}{8} + 3 = -\frac{5}{8}$

18. $-.03 + -.63 = -.66$

ANSWERS: WORKSHEET 2-22

1. $-3 \times 3 = \mathbf{-9}$
2. $5 \times -5 = \mathbf{-25}$
3. $-7 \times -2 = \mathbf{14}$
4. $8 \times -5 = \mathbf{-40}$
5. $-9 \times -6 = \mathbf{54}$
6. $10 \times -3 = \mathbf{-30}$
7. $-4 \times -6 = \mathbf{24}$
8. $-1 \times -1 = \mathbf{1}$
9. $-2 \times 1 = \mathbf{-2}$
10. $-3 \times 8 = \mathbf{-24}$

11. $\frac{1}{3} \times -\frac{1}{4} = -\mathbf{\frac{1}{12}}$

12. $-\frac{3}{5} \times \frac{5}{6} = -\frac{15}{30} = -\mathbf{\frac{1}{2}}$

13. $-1\frac{3}{7} \times -3\frac{1}{4} = -\frac{10}{7} \times -\frac{13}{4} = \frac{130}{28} = 4\frac{18}{28} = \mathbf{4\frac{9}{14}}$

14. $-6 \times \frac{5}{8} = -\frac{30}{8} = -3\frac{6}{8} = \mathbf{-3\frac{3}{4}}$

15. $-3\frac{7}{8} \times -5 = -\frac{31}{8} \times -\frac{5}{1} = \frac{155}{8} = \mathbf{19\frac{3}{8}}$

16. $3\frac{3}{4} \times -4\frac{1}{2} = \frac{15}{4} \times -\frac{9}{2} = -\frac{135}{8} = \mathbf{-16\frac{7}{8}}$

17. $-1.55 \times 7.2 = \mathbf{-11.16}$

18. $-3.007 \times -6.4 = \mathbf{19.2448}$

19. $9.1 \times -.05 = \mathbf{-0.455}$

ANSWERS: WORKSHEET 2-23

1. $10 \div -5 = \mathbf{-2}$

2. $-56 \div -7 = \mathbf{8}$

3. $-49 \div 7 = \mathbf{-7}$

4. $64 \div -8 = \mathbf{-8}$

5. $28 \div -4 = \mathbf{-7}$

6. $-81 \div -9 = \mathbf{9}$

7. $36 \div -2 = \mathbf{-18}$

8. $-48 \div -8 = \mathbf{6}$

9. $-144 \div -12 = \mathbf{12}$

10. $44 \div 11 = \mathbf{4}$

11. $-\dfrac{2}{3} \div -\dfrac{4}{5} = -\dfrac{2}{3} \times -\dfrac{5}{4} = \dfrac{10}{12} = \mathbf{\dfrac{5}{6}}$

12. $1\dfrac{1}{4} \div -\dfrac{1}{3} = \dfrac{5}{4} \times -\dfrac{3}{1} = -\dfrac{15}{4} = \mathbf{-3\dfrac{3}{4}}$

13. $-3\dfrac{1}{8} \div -2\dfrac{4}{8} = -\dfrac{\overset{5}{\cancel{25}}}{\underset{1}{\cancel{8}}} \times -\dfrac{\overset{1}{\cancel{8}}}{\underset{4}{\cancel{20}}} = \dfrac{5}{4} = \mathbf{1\dfrac{1}{4}}$

14. Mick had some custom T-shirts made for his band. The shirts cost $96.00. The band only saved up $78 for the shirts. After Mick pays for the shirts, how much money will the band have?

    $-96 + 78 = -18$ **The band now has -18 dollars.**

ANSWERS: CHAPTER 3 REVIEW TEST

1. $-9 + 14 = \mathbf{5}$

2. $-43 + -81 = \mathbf{-124}$

3. $90 + -45 = \mathbf{45}$

4. $-1.05 + 9.6 = \mathbf{8.55}$

5. $-\frac{3}{5} + -\frac{2}{10} = -\frac{8}{10}$

6. $432 - 987 = \mathbf{-555}$

7. $-17 - -5 = \mathbf{-12}$

8. $-23 - 14 = \mathbf{-37}$

9. $104 - 16 = \mathbf{88}$

10. $-4\frac{1}{2} - -3\frac{1}{3} =$
$-\frac{9}{2} - -\frac{10}{3} =$
$-\frac{27}{6} + +\frac{20}{6} = -\frac{7}{6} = \mathbf{-1\frac{1}{6}}$

11. $5\frac{1}{8} - -2\frac{1}{4} =$
$\frac{41}{8} + +\frac{9}{4} =$
$\frac{41}{8} + \frac{18}{8} = \frac{59}{8} = \mathbf{7\frac{3}{8}}$

12. $.023 - 5.2 = \mathbf{-5.177}$

13. $-5 \times 8 = \mathbf{-40}$

14. $7 \times -3 = \mathbf{-21}$

15. $-10 \times -90 = \mathbf{900}$

16. $\frac{7}{8} \times -\frac{5}{6} = -\frac{35}{48}$

17. $32.16 \times -3 = \mathbf{-96.48}$

18. $-14 \times \frac{1}{2} = \mathbf{-7}$

19. $-75 \div -3 = \mathbf{25}$

20. $-150 \div 2 = \mathbf{-75}$

21. $56 \div -7 = \mathbf{-8}$

22. $\frac{7}{12} \div -\frac{2}{3} =$
$\frac{7}{\underset{4}{\cancel{12}}} \times -\frac{\cancel{3}^{1}}{2} = -\frac{7}{8}$

23. $-\frac{6}{24} \div -\frac{18}{24} =$
$-\frac{\cancel{6}^{1}}{\cancel{24}_{1}} \times -\frac{\cancel{24}^{1}}{\cancel{18}_{3}} = \frac{1}{3}$

24. $-1008 \div 9\frac{3}{9} =$
$-\frac{\cancel{1008}^{12}}{1} \times \frac{9}{\cancel{84}_{1}} = -\frac{108}{1}$
$= \mathbf{-108}$

25. Keep track of Melodee's money. She received $100 for her birthday. She spent $41.39 at the store. She went to the gas station and spent $44.91 putting gas in her car. She received $25.00 for babysitting and gave her little brother $5.00 for washing her car. How much money does Melodee have left?

$100.00 - $41.39 - $44.91 + $25.00 - $5.00 = **$33.70**

ANSWERS: FINAL TEST

Solve the following fraction problems. Reduce your answers to the smallest denominator possible and convert any improper fractions into mixed numbers.

1. $\quad 2\frac{3}{8} + 3\frac{19}{24} = 2\frac{9}{24} + 3\frac{19}{24} = 5\frac{28}{24} = 6\frac{4}{24} = \mathbf{6\frac{1}{6}}$

2. $\quad 4\frac{3}{7} - 5\frac{4}{8} = \frac{31}{7} - \frac{44}{8} = \frac{248}{56} - \frac{308}{56} = -\frac{60}{56} = -1\frac{4}{56} = \mathbf{-1\frac{1}{14}}$

3. $\quad 6\frac{3}{4} \times -7\frac{1}{4} = \frac{27}{4} \times -\frac{29}{4} = -\frac{783}{16} = \mathbf{-48\frac{15}{16}}$

4. $\quad -4\frac{1}{12} \div -\frac{21}{36} = -\frac{\overset{7}{\cancel{49}}}{\underset{1}{\cancel{12}}} \times -\frac{\overset{3}{\cancel{36}}}{\underset{3}{\cancel{21}}} = \frac{21}{3} = \mathbf{7}$

5. Which fraction is bigger? Cross multiply and then use a $< or >$ sign.

$$\overset{1760}{\frac{32}{44}} < \overset{2112}{\frac{48}{55}}$$

6. Chris bought a bag of chocolate candies. The bag had 20 pieces of candy in it. Chris gave Nick 5 of the pieces and he gave Tony 8 of the pieces.

a. Write a fraction that shows how much of the bag he gave to Nick.

$$\frac{5}{20} = \frac{1}{4}$$

b. Write a percentage to show how much of the bag he gave to Tony.

$$\frac{8}{20} = 8 \div 20 = .4 \; which = 40\%$$

c. Write a decimal number to show how much of the candy Chris has left. (Hint: write a fraction and then divide the numbers).

$$\frac{7}{20} = 7 \div 20 = .35$$

7.   Fill in the empty box to make all values equal.

Decimal number	Fraction	Percentage
1.0	$\frac{26}{26}$	100%

Find the arrow and name the measurement:

8.    $\frac{3}{16}$ inch

9.   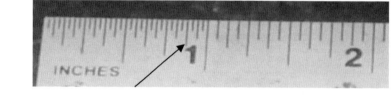 $\frac{7}{8}$ inch

10.    $1\frac{5}{8}$ inches

11.    $\frac{1}{32}$ inch